PROTECTING COWS

A HANDBOOK
OF
THE PRINCIPLES & PRACTICES
OF
VEGETARIAN COW HUSBANDRY

Compiled & Written
by
Syamasundara Dasa
(Stuart Coyle)

HATAGRA Publishing

First published in 1998 by
HATAGRA Publishing
24, Western Road,Hove.
Sussex BN3 1AF

ISBN 0 9525882 1 8

Printed & bound by Vision Printers, London N4 3NX.

DEDICATION

This book is dedicated to the cows of the world and those who wish to care for them.

ACKNOWLEDGEMENTS

I would like to thank the following friends for helping this book along at its various stages, for their encouragement, advice and practical assistance.

Devaki Suta for selling me his computer and for supplying me with many of the scriptural references., Ragamanjari for allowing him to do it, Isodyana for telling me to 'just type everything down', Tribhangananda for getting 'the book' out of my virused computer and on to a clean disk, Ali, who is 'crazy about the cows', for proof reading, Matthew for his invaluable comments, Archie for continually asking "when will it be finished?", Hladini Sakti for the paintings on the cover of the book, Ananta Sakti for his drawings, Kripamoya for undertaking the all-important final proof reading and Wenda, herself a protector of cows, for her un-ending enthusiasm; who lifted the book out of stagnation, brought it to fruition and who is now tirelessly promoting it.

Finally, I must offer special thanks to my wife, Lalita Sakhi and my children for their enduring patience during the research and the preparation of the first draft.

APPRECIATION

In 1966, a 70 year old Pure Devotee of Krishna appeared on the shores of the western world to reveal the truths of the ancient Vedic writings. In these books, the Vedas, Srila Prabhupada, as he is addressed by those who fondly know him, presented the principles and practices of protecting cows. This handbook is an attempt to compile and share some of those practical insights of Vegetarian Cow Husbandry.

This book has only been made possible because of Srila Prabhupada and I most humbly apologize to him for my paltry attempt.

Om ajnana timirandhasya
jnananjana Salakaya
Caksur unmilitam yena
tasmai Sri Gurave namah

His Divine Grace A.C. Bhaktivedanta Srila Prabhupada appeared in this world in 1896 in Calcutta, India. On meeting His Spiritual Master, Srila Bhaktisiddhanta Saraswati Goswami in 1922, He was convinced to dedicate His life to teaching Vedic knowledge, particularly to the english speaking world.

In fulfilment of His Spiritual Masters request, Srila Prabhupada arrived in New York City in 1965 and by 1966 He had established the International Society for Krsna Consciousness. Before His passing away on November 14th 1977, He guided the Society and saw it grow into a worldwide confederation of over one hundred "asramas", schools, temples, institutes and farm communities. Srila Prabhupada's most significant contribution however is His books. Highly respected by the academic world for their authoritativeness, depth and clarity, they serve as standard text books in numerous college courses.

Bhaktivedanta Manor is a Theological College for residential and non-residential students who wish to learn the philosophy and life style of Bhakti Yoga (Devotional Service to Lord Krsna).

In 1983, Europe's first Cow Protection Project was started at Bhaktivedanta Manor and has grown and developed since that time. This project offers a unique insight into the system of vegetarian, non-violent farming of cows and bulls.

FOREWORD

In 1975 I wrote and published a small pamphlet called "Europe's First Cow Protection Program." It referred to what was then going on at the Bhaktivedanta Manor goshalla. Srila Prabhupada called this mini-offering a "great service." I say mini-offering, because that's just what it was. I merely want to point out that these two written words of encouragement were sufficient to launch me on a career as a writer for the Krsna consciousness movement.

More important was the first-place significance our Founder-acharya gave to cow protection. Why would an eight page pamphlet be considered in Srila Prabhupada's mind a "great service?" The obvious answer is that it focused on Krsna cows, indispensable elements of Vedic and Brahmanical culture.

I consider Syamasundara's "Protecting Cows" a proper and comprehensive evolutionary sequel to my insignificant offering. Here is a book, which, based on both knowledge and years of experience, gives us an idea of what it means to protect cows and utilize ox-power in the Krsna consciousness movement.

Syamasundara's extensive research, his quotes from Srila Prabhupada's books and his many years of experience as a Krsna conscious herdsman really pay off in what is truly a "handbook" for devotees who are serious about raising and protecting cows.

There is a great need for a book of this kind, because cow protection is as much a science and an art as it is an eternal principle of Brahmanical and Vedic culture. Perhaps for the first time devotees will be able to use a standard book of knowledge to apply the simple but important mathematics of cow husbandry to raise and maintain a herd on an ISKCON farm.

These and many other practical and useful instructions make "Protecting Cows" an indispensable volume for all ISKCON goshallas worldwide. In writing this handbook, Syamasundara dasa has indeed performed a very great service.

Mukunda Goswami
ISKCON Governing Body Commissioner.

Introduction

When I was given the responsibility of looking after the cow and bull programme at Bhaktivedanta Manor it became very apparent that I needed some authoritative reference material about Vaisnava cow husbandry. In particular, there was a long standing area of disagreement between the men and women of the cow department and other members of the community. Specifically the cows were being managed along modern dairying lines in that the calves were being separated from their mothers after three days and no longer allowed to suckle milk directly from the milk bag. This needed to be looked into.

In Krishna's childhood He was given the task of herding calves and when He was older He was given charge of the cows. In fact He was displaying His eternal pastimes with the cows. Pastimes which go on equally in the transcendental realm, in Goloka Vrndavan. This is clearly described in the Srimad Bhagavatam and in particular the 10th Canto which Srila Prabhupada has presented as "Krishna Book".

The Krishna Book then became a mine of practical information regarding the practicalities of cow husbandry. The issue of the calf suckling from its mother is clearly explained within the Srimad Bhagavatam and other Vaisnava literature. The calf is kept separate from its mother during the day, by the cow and the calf being pastured in separate places, and at night, by the cow and the calf being kept in different pens. However the calf is allowed to drink milk directly from its mothers udder at milking time. The milkman ensures there is sufficient milk left in the udder to fully satisfy the calf.

The discovery of so much practical information excited me. I felt that I needed to compile and pick out all the practical instructions to ensure that the cow programme continued along authorised lines. It seemed that these instructions whilst present within the books should be clearly presented for use by any person dealing with cows. This handbook then has been written as an easy reference for most practical cow related issues.

I must apologize to all the established cow protecting devotees for my impudence at submitting this work as a handbook on cow husbandry. I appreciate the limitations of this book but I hope that it will have some value to all those who are interested in cow protection.

I have not gone into the full economic and sociological implications of cow protection. This has been left to other ardent writers. Within this handbook you will find evidence of the cow/calf relationship; how the calf can have access to its mothers udder without drinking all the available milk; information about the piercing of a bull's nose so that it can be controlled; some ideas on the requirements of a cowshed are mentioned; a warning about uncontrolled breeding and what type of bulls should be kept for breeding purposes. I have also inserted a section on some names of Krishna's cows plus many other related subjects, including castrating the bulls.

Thank you for giving this book your attention.

Syamasundara dasa

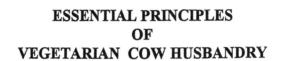

ESSENTIAL PRINCIPLES
OF
VEGETARIAN COW HUSBANDRY

1. Cows and Bulls must NOT be killed under any circumstance.

2. Calves MUST be allowed to suckle directly from their mother's udder until their natural weaning age of 7-10 months.

3. Cows MUST be hand-milked.

4. Bulls not engaged in a breeding programme should be trained in a respectful manner and their abilities utilised in a meaningful way. (e.g ploughing.)

5. Cows and bulls should be fed only natural vegetation - grasses, grains and suitable vegetables.

PROTECTING COWS

PHOTOGRAPHS

ILLUSTRATIONS

A COW'S DAY

This Chapter describes the basic methods of cow husbandry used every day based upon the system of daily management practised by Lord Krishna. Each aspect that is covered can be found in a quote mentioned further on in the handbook. Some details may need adjusting according to one's own circumstances, however the general principles can still be followed closely. Specific information on particular subjects can be found in the relevant chapters.

Milking the cows in the morning

Early in the morning, the cowherd men, women or children enter their respective cowsheds to milk their cows. The milkman brings the calf to the cow and allows it to take its required share. The rest is drawn off by the milkman. The system is such that the calf is initially brought to the cows udder to drink and when the mother has let down (released) her milk, the calf is then tied near to her head while the milkman has his share. The calf is then free to finish off all the remaining milk in the udder. The milkman having left sufficient milk for the calves' full satisfaction. As the calf gets older the amount of milk it needs diminishes as it becomes more and more satisfied with eating grass.

Pasturing the cows

In the morning the cows, calves and bulls go out to their respective pastures. There are many different gradations and they are all grazed accordingly. The young calves in one place, the older calves in another place, the cows in a different place. Even the adult cows are herded according to their colour.

These pasturing grounds and forests are selected because they have new grasses and different types of forage for the health and satisfaction of the cows. When one area is exhausted, the next day another place is chosen. Thus, as often as possible, the cows will always have fresh pasture to graze.

The young calves would be grazed in one place by themselves, separate from their mothers.

Young calves

The young calves are grazed in one spot by themselves, separate from their mothers. They are herded by the young boys. All these calves are practically the same age. There is a natural season when the bulls impregnate the cows and so the calves are usually all born within a couple of months of each other.

Older calves

The older calves which have already been weaned from their mothers, but which have not as yet had their own calf, are also grazed separately. These calves although larger and satisfied with only eating grass are kept apart from their mothers because they still have the tendency to drink milk from the udder. These older calves are herded by boys. They are larger than the ones just born and could intimidate the young ones if they were grazed together. Keeping the older and younger calves together can also cause herding and separating problems at milking time.

Young bulls

Young bulls come into sexual potency around seven or eight months or even younger and so, for this reason they may have to be kept away from older calves and also cows. In general though, an adult cow will not tolerate the immature advances of a young bull.

These young bulls may be grazed or tethered separately either at home or in the pasture, thus avoiding an unwanted pregnancy.

Older cows

The older cows which have all calved are grazed separately from their younger and older calves. They are herded by older boys and men. The cows are kept separate from the calves for the obvious reason that their calves would drink all the available milk. Once the older calves have had their first calf then they can join the main group of cows.

All the cows have their calves at practically the same time because the bulls generally impregnate the cows during the same period, namely autumn (for India). Western cows if left to themselves calve in time for the fresh spring grasses, having been impregnated in the summer.

Wandering potent bulls

There are some bulls which are religiously released to roam free. These bulls, full of semen, are allowed to wander as they please impregnating any cows which are ready. These bulls have been specially selected as being suitable to carry on desirable qualities in their offspring. Bulls unsuitable for procreation are castrated and used as oxen for working. Castration is carried out at between one and three years of age. This ensures that the growth of the young bulls is not hampered and that the oxen are as docile as possible. Leaving it too late would have no effect on the docility of the oxen.

Oxen

The oxen can be grazed separately or with the cows if they are not involved in working. Generally if left together the cows and oxen will stay apart naturally.

Herding in woods and watering the cows

During the day the herdsmen/boys take their cows or calves to selected pastures and forests. They have to avoid the land which is put aside for agricultural use. Whilst out, the cows and calves have to be watered as necessary, perhaps visiting a well or river two or three times a day. The herding of the cows in woodland and forests serves as a shelter against the heat of the sun, the rain or the cold. It also ensures there is a wide variety of forest foods and herbs.

After being out in the pasturing grounds for some time the boys bring back the calves to their homes and cowsheds. This is done before the adult cows return with the cowherdsman in the evening twilight.

Milking in the evening

On returning, the cows once again suckle their calves and the milk man takes his quota of the milk.

Housing separately

During the night the calves, older calves, cows etc., are all kept separate. They are tethered, or better still, housed in different enclosures allowing for freedom of movement. There the cows, bulls, oxen and calves can lay peacefully chewing the cud and eating what their keeper has put out for them, awaiting the coming of dawn when they will once again enter the pasturing grounds and forests.

"Young, brown, milk-laden cows, who were well-behaved, beautiful, endowed with good qualities, who were acquired honestly.
SB 10.64.13

CHOOSING A COW OR BULL

Young, brown, milk-laden cows, who were well-behaved, beautiful, endowed with good qualities, who were all acquired honestly.
SB 10.64.13

All glories to Lord Krishna's pet bull Padmagandha, whose handsome horns are covered with gold and studded with pearls; whose hooves are splendidly decorated with sapphires and whose splendid neck is decorated with a swinging garland of reddish flowers. VVS.

Even the poorest of the householders keep at least ten cows, each delivering twelve to twenty quarts of milk. SB 1.19.39

Better to keep cowshed vacant than have a troublesome cow.
Bengali proverb

One may be well-versed in all the transcendental literature of the Vedas, but if he fails to be acquainted with the Supreme then it must be concluded that all of his education is like the burden of a beast or like one's keeping a cow without milking capacity.
SB 11.11.18

Rearing of animals is a virtuous deed. It is of two kinds, such as (i) effecting the amelioration of the beasts and (ii) their sustenance and protection. It is proper to effect the amelioration of all useful animals. Without help from the beast the family affairs are not well conducted. So care should be taken to improve their size, strength and nature. They are improved, when they are kept in particular conditions and suitably coupled for the breeding up of strong offspring. It is necessary to effect the improvement of bovine cattle more than that of any other beasts. With their help the cultivation work and the transit of loads from one place to another can be well conducted. Cows should be made to bring forth good calves from stout and strong and good-looking bulls. It is for this reason that bull calves are given liberty and freedom from work at the time of the shraddha ceremonies in honour of the 'manes' or deceased ancestors. These bulls at liberty, roving at large, grow huge in size and strong in the body and become fit for the procreation of a strong bovine race. As the animals do much service to the families, they should be nourished with good and sufficient fodder and lodged in good sheds. SCS 2.2 Virtuous deeds.

Selecting a cow

In whichever country you live there will be a variety of cows to choose from. Careful consideration must be given to selecting a cow who can deliver sufficient milk of good quality, and produce strong bulls. Ideally, she should be both beautiful to look at and very good-natured.

Parents mark their offspring

You may have difficulty in finding a cow who meets all these criteria, but the more you can get right the better. An ill-chosen cow or bull will mark its offspring and their calves in turn. Some bulls have particular markings which will be passed down through their issue. More importantly, a bull, or a cow, from low milk-yielding parents is likely to transmit the same low yielding potential to its offspring. Some breeds are also notoriously bad tempered and hard to handle. All these points should be borne in mind when acquiring a cow or a bull.

Beauty however, is in the eye of the beholder and what one person deems beautiful may not appeal to another.

Points to consider in choosing a cow

Don't accept any cow just for the sake of it being a cow. **When choosing a cow a number of issues require careful thought.** Take into account some of the following considerations:

- quantity of milk
- quality of milk (richness)
- ease of milking (teat size for example)
- docility and temperament
- colour markings
- strength of working bulls
- general health (good hooves for example)
- disease resistance
- weather tolerance
  (can it stay outside all winter, all summer)

Breeding responsibility

Keeping a cow and breeding from it, is like taking the responsibility for conceiving children. Can you ensure protection for future generations? Remember, if you want milk there will have to be calves, and thus the number of animals in your care will increase. This must be considered. You should make provision not only for your 'founding' cows but also their young. This is especially important in our present day cow-killing society.

Hereditary markings in the offspring

The characteristics, or at least some of them, from the original cow and bull will be passed down the line of adult to calf. Therefore, if the start of your herd has undesirable qualities (particularly in regard to milk quantity and quality and strength of bulls) then you may see those same qualities reflected in their calves, grand calves and great grand calves even if you are careful about breeding from then on.

Your 'founding' cows and bulls should, as far as possible, be very carefully selected .

Modern breeds of cows

Some modern types of cow have been bred with only one aim in mind; either a high milk yield (such as Holsteins) or for slaughter (Belgian Blue). There are also some breeds which are well known as draught animals (Sussex, Devons).

Oxen from some of the specific dairy breeds may not be suitably built for working and similarly cows from the more muscular breeds may not deliver sufficient milk.

These points should be borne in mind when selecting cattle for the purpose you desire. Generally, if anticipating caring for your own animals much consideration must be given to your own specific, personal requirements - e.g. milk cows or draught oxen. Traditional dual-purpose breeds are recommended as they usually combine a good milk yield with strong bulls.

Different Breeds

Throughout the world there are probably thousands of breeds, each with their own specific characteristics. For this reason it would be impossible to mention all the varities of cows and their particular attributes within the contents of this book. Suffice to say there is vaulable resource material available in each country that this book will be read, which will afford you more in-depth information on the various breeds available to suit your needs and environment. It is for this reason that I am trying to keep the information contained in this handbook as general as possible.

One fact which cannot be overlooked is that a cow which proves suitable for one place may not do well in another.

THE COWSHED

After entering the village, Vrndavana, all the calves entered their respective cowsheds, and the boys also went to their respective mothers and homes.

KB ch.13 para 8

In Vraja the surabhi cowbarns have crystal walls, enormous gold pillars and emerald roof beams. The roofs are made of various jewels with ruby-capped pillars. White as the deity of the goddess Saraswati, and sober and grave like great ascetics, splendid surabhi cows wander in the courtyards of these barns.

VRC.

Elderly cows are taken care of by the men, and the calves are taken care of by the boys; and as far as possible, the calves are kept separate from the cows, so that the calves do not drink all the available milk.

KB ch.13 para 12

As the animals do much service to the families, they should be nourished with good and sufficient fodder and lodged in good sheds

SCS 2.2. Virtuous deeds.

How special the cows are to Krishna and society. They should be kept in the most opulent and pristine facilities. Although they are happy outside with a little shelter we should endeavour to shower on them all comfort and attractive surroundings. Indeed we should worship them by our care.

Separate housing

Govinda divides the cows in different categories: the mothers having new offspring, those having older offspring (several months old), those in their mating season, those having many calves, the bullocks and the calves, as well as the bulls and the buffaloes. Each are grouped separately.

GL 19.99/100

11

Separation of different types of cows in different conditions is a basic part of cattle herding. Each type of cow needs its own shelter and feeding arrangements.

Required cow pens

The following list of designated pens takes into account the individual housing requirements of animals at different stages of growth and/or gender. Wherever possible and when space allows, this should be implemented.

Cow pen	- cows which have calved
Calf pen	- calves from birth to weaning age (0-10 months)
Older calf pen	- older female calves from weaning until they have their first calf (10 months - 2- 2 1/2 years)
Bull pen	- uncastrated bulls used for procreation
Oxen/bullock pen	- working males
Older male calf pen	- these young bulls will be from the age of weaning until they can join the older oxen or bulls. Some may be castrated between one and three years (depending on temperament) and some kept as stock bulls for breeding.

Area required for each animal

As a general guide, an area of between 1.2m² - 1.8m² per 100kg of body weight will provide sufficient space for housing each animal under cover.

An outside yard with unrestricted access should also be made available so that they can feel the weather on their backs if they wish. A yard area of similar size to that of the under cover housing will be adequate to meet their needs.

Storage facilities

Apart from animal housing, you will also have to consider provision of space for the following:

- hay and straw storage
- grain, fodder and vegetable storage for feed
- store rooms for various equipment including cleaning, medical and maintenance
- milking area
- watering area
- manure storage
- agricultural equipment
- quarantine area for sick animals

Aspects of the shed

The cow facility should provide shelter from the sun, wind and rain. Plenty of fresh water must always be available for the cows to drink as well as for keeping everything impeccably clean. You will also need a good drainage system in the floor to take away all the run-off water and urine. See how other farmers have created facilities for their cows and modify your cowshed as necessary. One point to remember is that modern sheds are not built with the Vedic principles in mind, so careful consideration should be given to ones exact requirements.

FEEDING THE COWS.

Although you are eating green grass every day, you are not filling your milk bag so we can utilise your milk....
    A cow eats green grasses in the pasture and fills her milk bag with sufficient milk so that the cow herdsman can milk her.
SB 4.17.23 purport.

As described in a previous verse, cows and other animals should be given sufficient grass to eat.
SB 4.17.25 purport

She (the cow) was hankering after some grass in the field.
SB 1.17.3

The cow, for instance, gives milk, but she does not drink that milk; she eats grass and grain, and her milk is designated as food for human beings.
Isopanisad vs.1

Anywhere you can keep a cow it will eat vegetables and grass.
SP lect. SB 1969

When there is sufficient grain production, the general populace eats the grains, and animals like cows, goats and other domestic animals eat the grasses and grains also.
SB 4.18.8. purport

I think that we should all go to the forest known as Vrndavana,where just now there are newly grown plants and herbs. It is very suitable for pasturing ground for our cows... Near Vrndavana is Govardhana Hill, which is very beautiful, and there is newly grown grass and fodder for the animals, so there will be no difficulty in living there.
KB ch.11 para 10

All the cowherd boys would daily go to the bank of the river Yamuna to water their calves.
KB ch 11 para 16

14

A cow eats green grasses in the pasture and fills her milk bag with sufficient milk so that the cowherdsman can milk her.

SB 4.17.23 purport

15

Straw eaten by a cow produces milk.
CC adi lila 6.14/15

The best presentation offered by Govardhana Hill was the newly grown grasses for the cows and calves.
KB ch21 para 12

The cows, being fed by new grasses (because of the autumn rains) became very healthy and their milk bags were all very full.
KB ch 20 para 17

What foods to give:

From the above quotations, we can see that the ideal foods for cows are:

GRASSES - This is the main and best food for cows. If you can arrange a variety of grasses for your cows to graze they will be happy and healthy. Different grasses have different healing and nutritional properties so variety is important.

The best way to feed your cows is by pasturing them in the grassy fields. Preferably one should take the cows and bulls to a different pasturing ground or field each day where there is an abundance of fresh green grass. Permanent pastures should contain a variety of natural herbs and vegetation which the cows will select as dictated by their individual needs. If permanent pastures are not available with such a variety of herbs etc., then these could be specifically cultivated and sown with a herbal mix amongst the grasses and clovers.

Unfortunately, grass will not grow all the year round, so dried grasses (hay) are generally given at such times. Hay is grass which has been cut and dried during the summer months when the grass is long and the sun is hot. The hay is then stacked and stored for use in winter.

HERBS AND WILD VEGETATION (FODDER) - It is interesting to note how woodlands and forests were very important in the grazing of cows. These areas would have had an abundance of different herbs and vegetation for the satisfaction and health of the cows, as well as offering shelter from the elements.

Densely growing forests offer sparse amounts of low-growing vegetation for feed, whereas thinly planted trees or parklands have an abundance of grasses growing with the additional benefit of leaf fodder and overhead cover.

GRAINS - There are a wide variety of grains which can be given to cows. Such grains increase the milk yield of the cows and give the bulls more strength for working the land. These grains may be the excess from that which is grown to feed people or else they could be grown specifically for the cows.

STRAW - Straw is left over from the grain harvest. In most cases, it can be eaten by the cows and has some nutritional value. Some types of straw are more suitable for use as bedding. Barley straw, oat straw and rice straw can be eaten, whereas wheat straw has very little nutritional value and thus is better suited for use as bedding.

VEGETABLES - The cows will enjoy eating a variety of vegetables. Root vegetables will need washing and chopping up into small pieces to avoid any danger of choking. The choice of vegetables you can offer your cows will depend very much on those freely available in your country of residence.

SALT.

Commercially processed food

Many atrocious substances are routinely fed to cows disguised as Nutritional Concentrates. Calf feed and "grower" (a high protein fattening food used primarily for beef production in store cattle) has been found to contain chicken manure, cardboard, bovine flesh and bone, fish oils and even human excrement! Far from being beneficial to the animals to whom this is fed, it is now an accepted fact that its consumption is in part if not wholly responsible for such devastating diseases as BSE in cattle.

BSE and the ensuing "cull"of innocent animals has cost the lives of millions of cows, calves and oxen world-wide. A sad example of mans reticence to face up to his responsibility for his actions.

Since the end of the Second World War, countries such as Britain have looked for a cheap, readily available source of protein to boost the growth of animals bred for meat production. With total disregard for any moral issues, such as feeding animal bi-products to herbivores (which is totally unnatural), young beef calves in particular have been reared on a diet so high in protein that within eighteen months if not sooner, they are ready for slaughter.

Recent legislation has begun to address the problems caused by feeding concentrates to cows banning the use of many of these so-called ingredients and implementing a strict labelling system for all prepared feed stuffs. Fish oil though is still routinely found as "protein" within these feeds.

My advice is to avoid all feed which is not completely natural. Do not be inclined to give your cows any processed food. Grass, hay, grains, straw and selected root vegetables are the perfect combination to keep any cow healthy and happy. Ultimately, the cows well-being is the goal for which you should strive.

Summer and winter feeding.

In summer, the cattle will, assuming they have access to adequate grazing, produce milk and some power (in the case of oxen) solely from eating fresh grass and vegetation. High-yielding cows and hard-working bulls will require supplementary feeding, especially grains.

In winter, when grass may not be available they will need feeding with some form of stored food such as hay or straw. The exact quantity each animal will require will depend on the type, breed and gender as well as on what is expected of them in regard to giving milk or working as draught oxen.

Winter feeding for maintenance or production.

If you simply want to maintain your cows and not expect much from them in terms of providing milk or working ability then feeding hay and/or straw as the main food will be adequate, albeit your animals would be happier with more variety. Infact the herdsman, out of affection for his/her animals wants to feed them as well as possible.

If you require milk from your cows and you want your bulls working hard, then a selection of the whole variety of listed foods would be ideal. The more productive they are the more grains and perhaps vegetables, they will require.

As well as basic foods there are also other dietary requirements in the form of salt and possibly oil which should be considered.

Depending on how hard the bull is working and how much milk the cow is supplying, the feed quantities should be increased.

Balancing the ration

For optimum health and milk production, good rumination is required. This is dependent on foods which have long fibres (grass and hay) rather than short fibres (vegetables).

Vegetables are good for supplementing minerals, salts and vitamins. Root vegetables are best, particularly potatoes. They should, however only be classed as a supplement. Care should be taken not to over-feed them as this could result in stomach upset and interfere with healthy rumination, thus affecting the health, strength and milk yield of the cow.

The animals should always have access to plenty of grass, hay and/or straw.

Supplementary feeding for working oxen

For working oxen, the following supplementary feeding is suggested:

0.25 kg grain per hour for light work
0.50 kg grain per hour for medium work
0.75 kg grain per hour for heavy work

Feeding without grazing

A rough guide of how much hay to feed a cow or ox daily, if grazing is not available is as follows:

- a small cow (Jersey, approx. 380 kg) requires about 7kg
- a small milking cow 9kg
- a large cow (friesian, approx 560-650 kg) requires 9kg
- a large milking cow 12kg
- an ox (weighing approx 1000 kg) requires 12 kg

Feeding grains to milking cows

A milking cow should be offered about 0.35 - 0.4 kg of grain for each litre of milk she produces. If the milk is very rich (Jersey or Geurnsey), you should give 0.5 kg per litre. Suitable grains could comprise of a mixture of rolled or coarsely ground oats and barley and cracked or kibbled beans.

Different foods for cows in countries other than UK

For specific details of which foods to give and the quantities required, please research the native foods and farming systems available in your area. The following Table should be of some assistance when planning your feeding schedule based on available foodstuffs.

A table of food equivalents

1 kg of average hay =

    0.75 kg Very good meadow hay
    4.00 kg Kale, cabbage or other greens
    5.00 kg Mangolds, swedes or wet beet pulp
    3.00 kg Fodder beet or potatoes
    3.00 kg Silage
    2.00 kg Good feeding straw (barley/oat/rice)
    0.50 kg Grains or beet pulp

Warning regarding some foods

Certain foods, if over-fed or given too early on in an animals life can cause upset. An excess of grains fed either deliberately or by accident (which unfortunately I have experienced) can cause death. So too can the feeding of fruits. It is wise, if in any doubt to thoroughly check on the suitability of different foods and whether they can be used to feed cows and in particular calves.

LIVING LIFE TO THE FULL

How long does a cow live?

*How long the cow will live? Their maximum age is twenty years ....
There are many cows (who live) eighteen years, sixteen years or ten
years.*

SP RM CONV Paris Jun 11, 1974

The age to which a cow can live is not generally appreciated
by modern farmers or the general population. Because of today's
commercial farming methods it is quite uncommon to see an old
cow. Dairy cows today generally do not survive beyond seven years.
This short life-span has nothing to do with a natural demise but is
forced upon them by the slaughterhouse regime. The cow will have
about four or five calves in her life and will then be sent ruthlessly to
be slaughtered. If the calf is unfortunate enough to be surplus to
requirement, its demise will be even swifter. This book is directly
opposed to such barbaric practices.

*The cow's calf is not only beautiful to look at, but also gives
satisfaction to the cow, and so she delivers as much milk as possible.
But in the Kali yuga (* the present age*), the calves are separated from
the cows as early as possible for purposes which may not be
mentioned by these pages of Srimad Bhagavatam. The cow stands
with tears in her eyes, the sudra milkman draws milk from the cow
artificially and when there is no milk the cow is sent to be
slaughtered. These greatly sinful acts are responsible for all the
troubles in present society.*

SB 1.17.3. purport

A cow, if left to see out its full life, can live for around 15-
20 years, or even longer. This is an important point to consider when
planning out your breeding programme. As the above quote at the
top of the page points out there will be some cattle which will live
much less than fifteen or twenty years. One must make provision for
the cows and bulls in their old age.

The cows calf is not only beautiful to look at, but also gives satisfaction
to the cow..........
SB 1.17.3 & purport

Old age and death

As your cow approaches its end it may show similar symptoms as would affect a human being; a general weakening of its limbs and faculties which may lead to complete immobilisation. The cow or bull will 'go down', (be unable to get up). Then, it is only a matter of time before it passes away. This can most certainly be a tearful time for the handlers and protectors.

During this period one can make provision to alleviate the suffering as much as possible but one must not think of ending the cow's life prematurely. The soul has a certain time allotted to it in that particular cow's body and to interfere with it would reap personal responsibility as well as cause the soul to enter again into the body of another cow to complete its time.

What do you do with the body?

In the Vedic culture nothing is wasted and so traditionally there would be people to fully utilise the various parts of the dead cow's body - the cow's skin for leather, for example. Srila Prabhupada has said that the meat-eaters can eat the flesh of the cow once it has died.

Normally though, those who have spent many years looking after their cows may want to take care of the body themselves, by burning or burial.

At Bhaktivedanta Manor where we have only a small herd which we all feel very close to, we have a small ceremony. A deep grave is dug and the cow placed inside. We read some stories of Krishna's pastimes with the cows, say a few words about the cow and then circumambulate the body accompanied by Kirtan. The cow is then buried.

With a very large herd such ceremonies may not be practical for each and every cow.

BREEDING - INCREASING THE HERD

This chapter addresses some of the practical considerations of breeding cows. As we will see, the practice of annual calving during Krishna's time, may not be feasible today and a practical alternative method is described.

In the passages of the Srimad Bhagavatam, and other Vedic literature, the system of impregnating cows was left primarily to the meeting of wandering fully-potent bulls.

He (Uddhava) approached Vrndavana at sunset, when the cows were returning home after the pasturing ground...... He saw bulls running after cows for mating......
KB ch. 45 para 10

Are these great boulders from the crystal mountain? Are they tidal waves from the milk ocean? These are the bulls of Vraja. During the day they freely wander, just like liberated souls, and during the evening they sit peacefully at home, just as great sages rapt in contemplation. Proudly mooing from the loose folds of skin about their necks, Vraja's bulls look just like old sanyasis. Then again, their reddish stares make them look like intoxicated persons.
VRC

These wandering potent bulls would have been purposely selected for having suitable physical qualities wanted in the offspring.

Cows should be made to bring forth good calves from stout and strong and good-looking bulls....These bulls at liberty, roving at large, growing huge in size and strong in the body, become fit for the procreation of a strong bovine race.
SCS ch.2 sec.2 Virtuous deeds BT

Specially selected bulls for breeding and release

Not just any bull would be allowed freedom to roam. Only bulls which could pass on improved qualities in the cattle would be selected.

Are these great boulders from the crystal mountain?
VRC

26

Although in India today one will still see wandering bulls, this would not be practical elsewhere. The rest of the world will probably use bull pens where the fully potent bulls are kept. Should there be a number of cows who need impregnating the bull will be released to run with them.

Cows impregnated yearly

Free-roaming bulls meant that practically every cow would be impregnated annually. A cow would have a calf every year and thus start a fresh lactation.

On arrival of the autumn season, all the cows, deer, birds and females in general became pregnant, because in that season generally all the husbands became impelled by sex desire.
KB ch.20 para 22

European and American cows would naturally calve in spring if allowed to have constant access to a bull.

Large numbers of cows...
A burden or a sign of wealth....?

As far as I have found, Vedic society did not seem concerned by increased herd size. Rather such numbers were a measure of wealth, both for the family and society.

Although a whole book could be written on the practicalites of unrestricted procreation in regard to the apparent uncontrolled breeding demonstrated in the Vedic culture, perhaps it is easier to accept that nature made the necessary adjustments to the numbers, or simply that the total herd numbers matched the needs of the growing populace.

Working oxen are at the heart of a stable economic society based on Cow Protection.

One clear understanding is that when Krishna displayed His pastimes on Earth, the ox was a much sought after commodity for power and transportation. When there is a great demand for working bulls then there is a great demand to impregnate cows.

Historically society was dependant on the ox.

Dependance on the ox continued throughout the centuries until relatively recently when the horse took over. More recently, the tractor replaced the horse.

A change in attitude

In this day and age when cow protection is not appreciated, herd size must be carefully managed according to ones resources of land, money and manpower. Due to the over-use of tractors which get larger and larger and the subsequent decline in smaller farms, hardly anyone is willing to care for the bulls, much less work them. Tractors completely replace the need for working bulls. They also severely minimize the number of people needed for agricultural work.

Working oxen means working men

To work oxen there must be a commitment of manpower. For practical reasons, for each team of two oxen there should be one or better still two men. Without sufficient manpower one cannot work all the bulls. Today, labour is very expensive and food undervalued, at least in the so-called developed world. For this reason, it is extremely difficult to make ox-powered farming pay on its own merits. However working oxen fits in perfectly with a natural self-reliant lifestyle or a simple life without great financial needs.

The present emphasis on cattle in society is for milk production and slaughter. If an animal cannot give sufficient milk then it is a prime candidate for the slaughterhouse. Practically all the bulls are slaughtered soon after birth.

The test of a healthy cow protection society

A friend once recounted how cows were cared for in his home village in India. What he said was very interesting and significant. It suggests a symptom of a cow orientated society. He said, "when a calf is born there is more happiness if the calf is a bull rather than a cow".

Working oxen means working men.

His reasoning behind this statement was that as his village was so reliant on bulls for transport and draught work there was no difficulty in finding employment for them. Thus they could be sold. Vedic tradition ensured that these males would be allowed to live their lives free from fear of the slaughterhouse.

There was a demand to impregnate the cows because all of the offspring could be found work, providing milk or as draught oxen.

Having cows is like having children.....
..... We MUST do it....

Our present values and economics dictate that it is as great a responsibility to impregnate cows, as it is to conceive children. On the other hand, it is essential (according to Vedic tradition), to drink milk from the cow and derive our food from land which has been tilled by the bull. The burden of keeping cows is important to society and therefore we should strive untiringly to find the means to best protect cows not only in these difficult times but for the future.

Herd composition

Suppose you have sufficient land (about 2 1/2 - 3 acres per animal), money and manpower to completely maintain twenty cows/bulls. Let us surmise for the pupose of this exercise, that the size of the herd has been obtained by impregnating one cow per year, thus producing one calf annually. Taking into account that cows can live for a period of twenty years (see Chapter 5),then the composition of your herd will be as follows:

0-1 year old   - one calf, just born male/female
1-2 years old   - one bull calf & one female calf
3-15 years old   - six bulls/oxen and six cows
16-20 years old - five retired bulls/oxen and/or cows

Total: twenty bulls/oxen and cows

Commercial breeding and milking practices

Modern farming and the Vedic system are similar in that a cow gives milk for a ten month period (lactation).

The cow needs about a two month rest before her next calf is born.

Of course one vital difference is that in the Vedic System, calves would have been allowed regular suckling from their mothers until weaning age (7-10 months). Commercial dairy farming methods separate the calves from their mothers at 3/4 days if not earlier.

Referring to the herd composition list it can be seen that if one cow is giving milk then there are nineteen others who are not. Imagine if you were to let every cow in your herd have a calf each year. The herd would become increasingly larger, putting a greater strain on available resources. Numbers must therefore be stringently controlled.

To make the herd composition more useful and wholesome, some steps need to be taken

Lengthening the cows lactation

The cow which has calved should be encouraged to give milk for longer than the normal 10-month lactation. At least two or three years is certainly possible for today's western cows. There are numerous examples within the 'International Society for Krishna Consciousness' and elsewhere, of cows whose lactation has been extended to two years, three years, eight years and even twelve years.

A human mother can breast-feed her child for five years without difficulty if she wants to. She merely has to keep breast-feeding. Similarly, if you keep milking the cow she will keep producing milk, at least to some degree.

Can your cow give milk for six years?

If you can keep your cows milking longer, then, using the herd composition list, it is conceivable that you could have all six of the adult cows giving milk, albeit at different levels, providing you can keep the lactation going for about six years.

Assuming your cow has its first calf at the age of two/two and a half (the best age for the first calving) and she has her second calf at eight or nine years old then the optimum length of a lactation would be six years. You should therefore aim to keep as many of your cows as productive as possible without the need to increase the herd number.

In practice, getting a six-year lactation from all your cows may not be feasible, however two, three or even four years should generally prove no problem.

This experience of extended lactation is based on breeds of western cows. At present I do not know how lengthening lactations would work in Asian or African conditions.

Keeping the cows healthy in a long lactation

Keeping the cows milking long after their calf has been weaned may require some additional attention to the health and care of the udder (no longer having the calf suckle or agitate the milk bag). My own experience has shown garlic to be a potent udder tonic which may be fed on a regular basis or as required. It should be given crushed at milking time in order that it will not taint the milk. You may well find other herbs which will prove beneficial to the health of your cows udder.

I have not as yet found any difficulty in maintaining the health of a cow on a long lactation, at least no more so than normal. It is however, imperative that you know how to care for your cow should there be any illness.

Another point to consider in keeping a lactation maximized is that the cows routine should not be broken. Avoid any and all situations which may cause her alarm.

Daily milk yield

The amount of milk your cow supplies each day will probably decrease as the lactation extends. The most obvious difference being seen between the first and second year. I have heard that in Spain, there were cows who actually gave more milk in their second year than during the first. This however is not the norm. The same cows were kept milking for three years.

Although the seasons have an effect on the yield because they dictate the quantity and quality of the grass, it is your feeding programme which will have the greatest bearing on your cows milk yield.

I have found that the cow's daily milk delivery gradually diminishes practically month by month. By the end of the second year she will be giving one quarter of the milk that she initially gave (after the calf has had its fill, of course). Therefore a cow which gives fifteen to twenty litres after the birth of her calf would drop down to giving maybe three to five litres per day at the end of two years. Others however, giving ten litres at the start of their lactation might still be giving eight after two years. This information is based on my experience of Holstein/Friesian cows at Bhaktivedanta Manor. There are other documented cows which have given a steady supply of almost ten litres a day for three years.

Losing a cow before it is twenty

One factor which cannot be overlooked is that unfortunately, there will be instances of untimely loss of life in your herd from disease and accident etc. You must also remember that not every cow will live to be twenty; some will die naturally before then. This means that your breeding cycle could accomodate the possible requirement of impregnating a second cow in the same year.

If you are inseminating one cow each year and a calf is lost at birth, you could, to maintain your optimum herd total at say, twenty animals, put a second cow in calf. This would mean that more of the cows are productive. On the other hand, you could choose to accept the natural losses of your cattle as a means of keeping the numbers lower.

Cooperative family herds

If you want milk but need to keep your herd at a minimum, inseminate a cow once every three years. You should be able to get a three year lactation from your house cow. This way, with a new calf being born every thirty six months, your total herd size will not exceed seven cows/bulls. If you require more milk than your cow is producing during her low yield time, you could always get it from another farm with protected cows.

Working the bulls

At the risk of stating the obvious, meaningful engagment must be sought for the workable oxen. Such tasks might include:

- ploughing and tilling the land
- local transportation
- tourism and oxcart rides
- powering machinery via a draught unit.

This area is actually the crux of a healthy cow protection plan. If bulls are put to meaningful, valuable employment then milk production will be viable and economic. To have a breeding programme which cannot find regular work for the males is both unhealthy and extremely uneconomical.

Maximizing the usefulness of cow dung.

Two of the greatest resources from cows are their dung and urine. In the organic way of looking at farming and growing, it is worth keeping cows just for the dung, forgetting all the other attributes they have. The value of manure for fertilisation and land improvement is widely known. Other uses which increase its value are;

FUEL - provided directly from gas given off by the dung via a methane digester, or by burning the dried dung directly.

FERTILIZER - this could be dried and sold in bags in powdered form, or else sold as decomposed farm yard manure. Never mind selling it, just think of the benefit of that manure on your own land.

Charitable support

Make the bulls and cows recipients of charitable donations. Giving in charity for cows is a regular element of Vedic society.

This suggestion may be somewhat controversial for those seeking self-reliance, however I feel it is both important and helpful during the preliminary stage. At this present time there is great interest in supporting animal charities. Is there any animal so useful and thus so deserving of charitable support as the cow or the bull? Interested people could give money for the maintenance of a cow or bull for a week, a month, a year or even for life. Therefore the donor sponsors/adopts a bull or a cow. By accepting financial support and thus taking away the burden of making ones cows and bulls compete in the modern economic system, one is allowed the room to properly protect cows; by being able to draw milk from them, work the bulls in the field and offer them all a full, dignified and happy life.

In conclusion

To keep the Cow Programme running at maximum efficiency, cows should be encouraged to have longer lactations and all the working oxen should be employed. In fact, if useful employment is secured for all the oxen, cow protection will never be a burden, but an asset and a source of wealth.

COW'S MILK - THE MIRACLE FOOD

There are many quotes extolling the benefits of milk. I have submitted only a small selection which I find particularly striking.

There is a miracle in milk, for it contains all the necessary vitamins to sustain human physiological conditions for higher achievements. Brahmanical culture can advance only when man is educated to develop the quality of goodness, and for this there is prime necessity of food prepared with milk, fruits and grains.
SB 1.16.4

A pound of milk fresh from the milk bag of a cow is sufficient to feed an adult with all vitamin values, and therefore saints and sages live only on milk.
SB 1.19.39 purport

Milk is compared to nectar, which one can drink to become immortal. Of course, simply drinking milk will not make one immortal, but it can increase the duration of one's life. In modern civilization, men do not think milk to be very important, and therefore they do not live very long. Although in this age men can live up to one hundred years, their duration of life is reduced because they do not drink large quantities of milk......... The cow should be protected, milk should be drawn from the cows , and this milk should be prepared in various ways. One should take ample milk, and thus one can prolong one's life, develop his brain, execute devotional service and ultimately attain the favour of the Supreme Personality of Godhead.
SB 8.6.12 purport

The cow delivers more milk than is needed by the calf because milk is intended for man.
Matchless gifts 4

Mystic process of making milk from grass.
Life from life 6

MILKING THE COWS

Every morning at approximately 6.30 am, Sri Gopal enters Nanda Maharaja's cowshed to milk the transcendental cows. As Krishna calls to each cow, they respond by mooing and immediately surround Krishna. Then Sri Krishna bends down, holding a golden milk pail between His knees, and milks some cows. Krishna directs the cowherd boys to milk other cows, and He lovingly caresses the cows in between milking. Govinda also ensures that each and every calf drinks milk to its full satisfaction.

Govinda Lilamrta by Krishna Das Kaviraja

'O great hero, protector of living entities, if you desire to relieve the living entities by supplying them sufficient grain, and if you desire to nourish them by taking milk from me, you should make arrangements to bring a calf suitable for this purpose and a pot in which the milk can be kept, as well as a milkman to do the work. Since I will be very much affectionate towards my calf, your desire to take milk from me will be fulfilled'.

These are nice instructions for milking a cow. The cow must first have a calf so that out of affection for the calf she will voluntarily give sufficient milk. There must also be an expert milkman and a suitable pot in which to keep the milk. Just as a cow cannot deliver sufficient milk without being affectionate to her calf, the earth cannot produce sufficient necessities without feeling affection for those who are Krishna conscious.

SB 4.18.10 and purport

As small calves tied with ropes await anxiously the time of milking, when they will be allowed to drink the milk of their mothers. ... a small calf is not satisfied unless allowed to suck the milk from the mother's udder...

SB 6.11.26 and purport

Once upon a time, my poor mother, when going out one night to milk a cow...

SB 1.6.9

Krishna and Balarama come to our houses every morning and evening before the milking of the cows, they let loose the calves, and the calves drink all the milk.

SB 10.8.28

Krisnna and Balarama come to our houses every morning and evening before the milking of the cows, they let loose the calves, and the calves drink all the milk.

SB 10.8.28

The earth planet personified came as a cow, and, as though she saw her calf, she delivered milk profusely when she saw all the good qualities of Maharaja Gaya.

.... A cow delivers milk in the presence of her calf.
SB 5.15.10 and purport

Seeing a cow milked along side its calf is a good sign.
KB ch.44 para 15

A cow delivers more milk than is needed by the calf because milk was intended for man.
Matchless gifts 4

Cow's milk is not meant for the cow but for the human being. Cow will not drink milk.
BG lect 1966 SP

He (Akrura) reached Vrndavana by the end of the day... When he reached Vrndavana, the sun was setting... When Akrura entered Vrndavan, he saw Krsna and Balarama engaged in supervising the milking of the cows.
KB ch.37 paras 12 & 14

These cows had their own calves, and the calves that were grazing beneath Govardhana Hill were larger, they were not expected to drink milk directly from the milk bag but were satisfied with the grass...

...Elderly cows are taken care of by the men and the calves are taken care of by the boys; and as far as possible the calves are kept separate from the cows, so that the calves do not drink all the available milk.
KB ch.13 paras 11&12

A cow eats grasses in the pasture and fills her milk bag with sufficient milk so that the cowherdsman can milk her.
SB 4.17.23 and purport

.... and the calves that were grazing beneath Govardana Hill were larger, they were not expected to drink milk directly from the milk bag but were satisfied with the grass.

KB chap 13 para l

He (Uddhava) approached Vrndavana at sunset when the cows were returning home from the pasturing ground... He saw bulls running after cows for mating; other cows with overladen milk bags, were running after the calves to fill them with milk. Uddhava saw that the entire land of Vrndavana was filled with white cows and their calves, running here and there all over Gokula, and he could hear the sound of milking.

KB ch.45 para 10

There are many important points to consider regarding the calf's practical relationship with its mother. If you can follow the principles of making the cow and the calf happy then Krishna will be pleased, the milkman is pleased and society is pleased.

There are some similarities between Krishna's system of cow-keeping and today's. Note the differences and adjust your methods in favour of the natural system as taught and practised by Lord Krishna in His childhood activities.

Milking twice a day

Cows are generally milked twice a day, once during the early morning and then again in the evening when the herds come home from the pasturing grounds. From the verses on the previous pages, we can see that Krishna brought the cows back home at dusk.

The calves are brought to their mothers

At milking time bring the calves before their respective mothers to stimulate the 'letting down' of the milk. This may be accomplished in a number of ways:

1.   The calf may be allowed to suckle from its mother's udder for a few moments before you start milking. The calf can then be secured near its mother's head. It seems that Indian-type cows will not 'let down' their milk unless the calf has first been suckled.

2.   The calf can be placed near its mother's head initially until you have finished taking your share and then released to drink milk directly from the udder.

3.   The calf may also be kept in its pen where its mother can see it until you have taken your quota and then let loose to spend time with its mother.

The practicalities of where the calf is positioned during milking may vary from country to country and depend on the type of cow. Irrespective of which system is used, the most important point is that milk is saved in the udder for the calf and the calf drinks this milk directly from its mother, being allowed to stay with her for a suitable period of time. One can judge from watching when they lose interest in each other.

The milkman saves milk in the udder for the calf

The milkman takes his share of the milk, leaving sufficient for the calf's satisfaction. When the milkman/maid has finished milking, the calf which may have been secured alongside its mother, or kept separate, is now released to drink directly from its mother's udder. Mother cow very happily and affectionately licks and grooms her calf. There is a warming picture of the calf suckling contentedly from its mother standing in a parallel position. The relaxed mother pleasingly grooms the rump of her calf.

Our experience has shown that in most cases, the cow has the ability to let down milk for the herdsman whilst saving milk for her calf, therefore putting the cow in charge of rationing. This is service to the cow as opposed to exploitation and is not possible when a milking machine is used.

How much milk should the calf have?

The amount of milk required by the calf will vary according to age etc. A young calf generally requires 10% of its body weight in milk each day. A friesian calf weighing 45kgs will at first require 4.5kgs of milk. As the calf gets older it becomes less dependant on milk as it starts to eat grass and hay.

..... the calf suckling contentedly from its mother standing in a parallel position.

Roughly speaking, 25% of the total daily milk yield will be on one teat. After some weeks the quantity saved can be reduced or left as is appropriate. However, there must always be milk left in the udder for the calf.

As saving milk in the udder is an essential part of vegetarian cow husbandry, its importance cannot be stressed too often within the pages of this book.

Bucket feeding

Not only is bucket feeding a calf undesirable, it is unhealthy, unnatural and un-Vedic. It should only be done in extreme circumstances for example if the calf's mother has died and there is no foster mother available. Bottle feeding is by far the better option in such a situation.

The cows and calves are housed or pastured separately

Shortly after milking, the calves leave their mothers and join other calves to sport and play. They are kept in separate pens or pastures from their mothers. The calves will stay together, separate from the adult cows, until milking time comes around again in the morning or evening.

How to milk

There are many different methods of milking cows, depending on what part of the world one is from. However, the fundamental points are the same, even if the technique differs.

Washing the udder

Before milking, it is necessary to first wash the udder with warm water. This removes any dung or dirt which the cow might have picked up whilst laying down and which could contaminate the milk. Washing, like other routine tasks helps stimulate 'let down' from the cow who is by now happily waiting to be milked.

Milking - the Western system

Holding teats

The teats should be held firmly, but not too tightly. Indeed all movements near the udder should be firm and sure. Ticklish movements or holding the teats too lightly are often rewarded with a swift kick.

Milking - the Indian system

Apply pressure on the teat using the fingers and the knuckle of the thumb, this being pushed against the teat and then down the teat. The fingers remain on the other side. This squeezes the milk out.

Milking - the Western system

Squeeze the teat between the first finger and the thumb at the point where it joins the udder thus trapping the milk in the teat. The remaining fingers are then squeezed around the teat to expel the trapped milk. Release the grip allowing the milk from the udder to flow into the teat again. Squeeze first with the left hand and then with the right. Repeat with the left hand and so on.

To learn to milk with some degree of confidence and at a good speed will probably take a week of practice and a patient cow.

Small teat milking

Sometimes cows are found to have teats too small to milk in the conventional way. It is a modern breeding aim to engineer cows with smaller teats for ease of use with milking machines. I prefer bigger teats and don't use machines for milking cows.

In the case of a cow with small teats, milking by hand may be performed in the following manner: First lubricate the teats. One may use the milk itself although in practice something more greasy like ghee or oil is preferable. Grip the teat between thumb and finger(s) and slide down the teat thus expelling the milk.

46

The ideal milking position

Krishna would squat on the balls of His feet to milk. If you are unable to balance this way, then a small stool may be necessary. Usually a milking-stool is three legged for ease of movement. Resting one's head against the side of the cow, just in front of and against the back leg, while you are milking lets the cow know what you are doing and gives you fair warning of what she is about to do. By feeling her muscle movements, one can predict a possible kick or unwanted movement.

Milking machines

The modern method of using a milking machine is condemned within the pages of the Srimad Bhagavatam -

The cow stands with tears in her eyes, the sudra milkman draws milk from the cow artificially, and when there is no milk the cow is sent to be slaughtered.
SB 1.17.3 purport

From this quote it can be clearly understood that machines have no place in a Vedic/Natural milking parlour. Cows MUST be hand milked. The use of milking machines creates a false 'manpower' relationship with cows. In reality, one person should be milking no more than 10-13 cows. Modern dairies with machine milking apparatus, milking perhaps 100 cows are far removed from the system outlined in this book. Large herds of artificially milked cows usually means large numbers of unworked and I am sorry to say unwanted oxen/bulls.

Calves and milking machines

The cow/calf relationship suffers immeasurable damage from the use of milking machines. It is not possible to ensure that there is enough milk left in the udder for the calf. Machines also require the use of powerful and poisonous chemicals for their so-called cleaning. Indeed the use of such machines distances the milkman from the all important close affectionate handling of the cow who should be embraced and her chin gently scratched. Milking machines display an undeniable air of exploitation.

Extra food at milking time

At milking time, the mother cow will most likely appreciate something a little different to her normal grass or hay, such as grains or vegetables. By giving her such foods you will ensure she is occupied and content, thus making her easier and steadier to milk.
It will also serve as an incentive for the cow to enter the milking area.
Cows which are giving milk are fed according to their yields. (See Chapter Four).

Tying a cows legs during milking

Certain cows may require some form of restraint to prevent them from kicking over the milk bucket or indeed the milkman, at milking time.

The traditional method practised by Krishna and His cowherd friends was to tie the back legs of the cows using a small rope. This was secured just above the knees, probably using some form of slip knot for quick release.

Krishna and Balarama carried binding ropes on Their shoulders and in Their hands, just like ordinary cowherd boys. While milking the cows, the boys bound the hind legs with a small rope. This rope almost always hung from the shoulders of the boys and it was not absent from the shoulders of Krishna and Balarama.
SB Ch.21 para 14

At Bhaktivedanta Manor we have small gates which close behind the cow when she enters the milking stall. If necessary, the cows two rear legs can be secured to the gate, holding her firm.
Very often, after a cows first calf, some type of leg restraint will be required. After a few months when the cow has grown accustomed to being milked it will not be needed.

Embracing, scratching and brushing

After the cows have been milked they can be lovingly caressed and embraced. They enjoy being brushed down and being gently scratched under the chin.

The relationship between the cow and herdsman is very important. It is one of trust and love and of symbiosis - i.e they help each other. In the main, the herdsman is the servant of the cow, and if he deals with the cow nicely the cow will respond with love and co-operation and plenty of milk.

A regular routine

The importance of a regulated routine for the herding and milking of the cows cannot be over stressed, in fact in practical terms a well-regulated life is the basis for a peaceful life for the milkman as much as the cows.

The cows and bulls will respond to a routine of the same time, in the same place, by the same person, in the same way, every day.

Milk yield

Even the poorest of the householders keep at least ten cows, each delivering twelve to twenty quarts of milk (13-23 litres), and therefore no one hesitates to spare a few pounds of milk for the mendicants.

SB 1.19.39 puport

Cow gives 40 - 50lbs (18-22 litres) of milk a day
SB lect 1972 SP

It can be seen here that the milk yield mentioned is comparable to modern high-yielding cows. However it is also stated that in previous ages the cows gave more milk than today.

In Kali Yuga... the cow does not give as much milk as it used to give formerly.

SB 1.4.17-18 purport

Good grass - good milk

The yield of your cow will depend upon the breed and how it is fed. Specifically if the cow is fed with nutritious grass from the field, as well as being allowed to suckle its calf, it will give as much milk as possible.

Milk yields of different breeds.

Independent research should be carried out to ascertain the yields of the various breeds of cow. Listing all the different breeds and their yields is beyond the scope of this book.

What to do with the milk after milking

There are legal requirements in place in each country governing the treatment of milk before consumption and most certainly before selling any. One will need to contact the respective authorities in this regard. Basically the milk needs to be boiled and then kept refrigerated or as was done in the 'churn days' cooled down as soon as possible after milking.

The method of dealing with milk in a traditional village is noted as follows:

Just like Nanda Maharaja was keeping cows. Similarly there are many villages. So the system is: - they have got a big pan, and whatever milk is collected, put into that pan. It is being warmed. So they drink, the whole family members. They drink milk whenever they like. So whatever milk remains at night they have to convert it to yoghurt. The next day they use milk and yoghurt also as he likes. Then after converting the milk into yoghurt, still it remains. It is stocked. So when there is sufficient old yoghurt, they churn it and then butter comes out. So they take the butter and the water separated from the butter, that is called whey. Whey yes. So they... Instead of dhal they use this whey for chapattis. It will be very healthy and tasty.

SP conv N. Orleans 1st August 1975

50

A practical point of consideration is that boiled milk keeps longer than unboiled milk even when refrigerated.

Cleaning

After milking your cows, one should finish off by ensuring that all milking paraphernlia is scrupulously clean.

HANDLING COWS AND BULLS

Krishna sat with His flute tucked between His waist and the tight cloth on His right side, and with His horn bugle and cow-driving stick on His left.

SB 10.13.11

Animals cannot undergo austerity. Cow may push its head in a shop and although being beaten with a stick she will tolerate.

PQPA

Just as a cowherd boy keeps a stick in his hand to give protection to the cows.
Lord Siva's punishment was just like that of a cowherd boy, who keeps a stick to frighten his animals. It is commonly said that to give protection to animals, a stick is needed because animals cannot reason and argue. Their reasoning is 'argumentum baculinum'. Unless there is a rod, they do not obey.

SB 4.7.14 and purport

Both Krishna and Balarama were so restless that Their mothers Yasoda and Rohini would try to protect Them from cows, bulls, monkeys, water, fire and birds while they were executing their household duties.

KB Chap.8 para 12

Each cowherd boy was equipped with a stick, flute and horn as well as a lunch-bag, and each of them was taking care of thousands of calves.

KB Chap12 para 1

Bear in mind that a cow and more particularly a bull are extremely large animals. When fully grown, a cow may well weigh about 600 kgs. and a bull 1000 kgs. Their sheer size is in itself a cause for respect and caution. The cow is normally very docile, but still accidents may happen. For example a cow may suddenly get startled and run away causing anybody in its path to be swept aside. You must also be prepared for the fact that a certain number of your cows may have aggressive tendencies.

Another point to remember is that cows naturally have horns (albeit there are some exceptions), and as Canakya Pandit warned, " Never trust an animal with horns".

Krishna carried a stick

It is very interesting to note that Krishna did not magically move His cows around, but that He enacted all the practical methods of cattle husbandry, including herding His cows by the use of sticks. Of course Krishna was so enchanting to the cows that they came when He called, but still He carried a stick.

The stick serves a number of useful purposes:

1. Moving Cows.
   To encourage a cow to move forward you may have to tap it on the rump with your stick. By extending your arm with a stick in your hand you create a bigger barrier to contain a cow or direct it. Because the cow is scared of somebody carrying a stick it will comply more willingly with the herdsman's wishes.

2. Protecting people's property.
   In days gone by and even today in the third world, fencing is rare, and thus crops had to be protected from inquisitive and forage-hunting cattle.

3. Physical protection.
   This idea may seem a bit out-of-date to those of us living in the west, but historically cows were herded by people. Consequently men and boys were on hand to scare away any dangerous elements from the cattle. It is more reassuring to face a strange dog carrying a stick than being empty-handed.

This reference to the use of a stick in no way encourages or condones the abuse of animals.

Generally, a brahmana, woman, child, old man or cow is never regarded as punishable.
SB 9.9.30

Cows and bulls are objects of affection and respect. Any use of force must be carefully controlled, using only as much as is absolutely necessary. This force is not used for the sake of being brutal but for the care and protection of the cows and bulls and people's property. With the proper relationship your voice will prove to be sufficient guidance for your cows. When necessary a wave of a stick or even a tap to act as a reminder may be called for.

Cows respect gentle but firm handling and care should be taken not to cause them any undue disturbance.

HERDING THE COWS

Keeping the calves before them, they started for the forest.
KB Ch.12 para 1

Thus when Krishna calls out, "Hey Dhavali" (the name of a white cow) a whole group of white cows comes forward, and when Krishna calls "Hamsi, Candani, Ganga, Mukta" and so on, the twenty four groups of other white cows come.
SB 10.35.19 purport

...the cows, being unobserved, began to wander off on their own, entering farther and farther into the deepest part of the forest, allured by fresh grasses. The goats, cows and buffalo travelled from one forest to another and entered the forest known as Isikatavi. This forest was full of green grass, and therefore they were allured...
KB ch.19 para 1

While herding the very beautiful bulls and cows, the Lord, who was the reservoir of all opulence and fortune, used to blow His flute, and thus He enlivened His faithful followers, the cowherd boys.
It is mentioned herein that the beautiful cows and bulls were of various checkered colours - red, black, green, yellow, ash etc. And because of their colours and healthy smiling features, the atmosphere was enlivening.
SB 3.2.29 and purport

55

*...the cows, being unobserved, began to wander off on their own, entering
farther and farther into the deepest part of the forest......*

KB Ch.12 para 1

NAMING THE COWS AND BULLS

The cows taken care of by Krishna had different names, and Krishna would call them with love. After hearing Krishna calling, the cows would immediately respond by mooing, and the boys would enjoy this exchange to their hearts' content.

KB Ch.15 para 6

When Lord Krishna called them (the cows) by name, they immediately came to Him out of affection, and in their joyful condition the milk flowed from their bags.

KB Ch 20 para 17

Thus when Krishna calls out, "Hey Dhavali" (the name of a white cow) a whole group of white cows comes forward, and when Krishna calls "Hamsi, Candani, Ganga, Mukta" and so on, the twenty four groups of other white cows come. The reddish cows are called Aruni, Kunkuma, Sarasvati, etc; the blackish ones Shyamala, Dhumala, Yamuna, etc; and the yellowish ones are Pita, Pingala, Haritaki etc. Those in the groups with tilak marks on their foreheads are called Citra, Citra-tilak, and Cirgha-tilaka and Tiryak-tilak, and there are groups known as Mrdanga-mukhi (mrdanga head), Simha-mukhi (lion head) and so on.

SB 10.35.19 purport

To the surabhi cows who have strayed far away Krishna calls "Oh Pisangi! Oh Manikastini! Oh Pranatasrngi! Oh Pinesana! Oh Mrdanga-muhkhi! Oh Dhumala! Oh Sobali! Oh Hamsi! Oh Vamsi-Priya!

UN

Krishna lovingly calls "He-he! Padme, Rangini, Kanjagandhe, and Rambhel! He-he! Camari, Hikanjani, Kajjalakhi, and Shande! He-he! Bhramarika, Sunade, Sunande, Dhumre and Sarali! He-he! Kali, Pali, Shayame, Hamsi and Kurangi! He-he! Kapale, Godavari, Induprabhue, Shone, Syeni and Triveni! He-he Jamne, Candralike, Narmade and Gopati!

GL 19.23 +24

Mangala, Pingala, Ganga, Pishangi, Manikastani, Hamsi and Vamsipriya are the most important of the surabhi cows who are all very dear to Lord Krishna. LSSRKGD 109

57

Padmagandha and Pisangaksa are Krishna's pet oxen
LSSRKGD 110

Sunada, Yamuna, and Bahula are the most important of Srimati Radharani's pet surabhi cows. Tungi is her chubby pet calf.
LSSRKGD 197

The selection of names for the cows seems to follow practical descriptions of the cow; the names of the white cows each mean white;the names of the red cows each mean red and similarly, the yellow and black cows. The tilak cows (a mark on the head between the eyes), are so named because some have spotted tilak and some have crooked tilak.

It seems that one can name the cows according to their particular characteristics, colour, nature etc. Bhramarika means 'roving in all directions'.

From my research there doesn't appear to be a hard and fast rule which states that cows must have Sanskrit names. In practice though it seems most devotees do give their cows Sanskrit names.

When naming working oxen it is practical to give them each distinct short names to make driving them easier and less confusing for them.

*Thus when Krishna calls out "Hey Dhavali" (the name of a white cow)
a whole group of white cows comes forward.*

SB 10.35.19 purport

A SELECTION OF SANSKRIT NAMES
FOR COWS AND BULLS

ARUNI: The colour of the rising sun;tawny,red

BHIMA: The name of a warrior, from Mahabharat

BHRAMARIKA: A bee; one who wanders in all directions

BHUBRIT: Maintainer of the Earth

CAMARI: Female deer:Doe

CANDANI: (Having the characteristics of) Sandalwood
(colour/aroma)

CHANRALIKE: Moon

CHANDRAVATI: Moon-like beauty

CHITRAGREEVA: Spotted neck

CHITRANGA: Spotted body

CITRA: Bright, clear: variegated, spotted

CITRATILAKA: Having a tilaka mark

CITRITA: Decorated

DADHIPUTCHA: Tail as white as curd

DANTILA: Strong teeth

DEEPTAKSHA: Shining eyes

DHARMA: Religion

DHAVALI: White

DHUMALA: Smoke-coloured, purple

DHUMRE: Smoke coloured, grey. Purple; mixture of black and
purple.

DHUSARAKA: Grey colour

DIRGA TILAKA: with a long tilaka mark

GANGA: River Ganga in India (colour - light and muddy)

GODAVARI: River Godavari

HAMSI: Swan (-like)

HARITAKI: The yellow myrobalan tree

HARITALIKA: (of the colour of) a particular species of pigeon
known for its yellowish and greenish color

HIRANYAKA: Gold-like

JAYA: Liberation

KALI: Black, dark blue

KARUNA: Mercy

KUNKUMA: (of the colour of) kunkuma (vermillion) - Red

KURANGI: A deer

MRDANGA MUKHI: Drum-face (Mrdanga is an Indian drum)

60

MUKTA: Liberated (pearl)
NANDA: Happiness, pleasure;joy
NANDAKA: Giver of pleasure
*NANDI:*Lord Siva's bull
PADMAGANDHA: Smells like a flower
PADMANIDHI: A treasure
PADMI: Lakshmi - the Goddess of fortune
PINGALA: Reddish brown;tawny
PINGALAKA: Reddish brown
PISANGAKSA: Reddish-brown eyes. (aksa - eyes)
PISANGI: Reddish brown
PITA: Yellow colour; Topaz
PRAKARAKARNA: Straight ears
PRIYADARSHANA: Sweet face
SARALI: Straight
SARASVATI: Name of Goddess/River - colour of - yellowish
SHANKUKARANA: Ears like wedges
SHEEGHRAGA: Fast-moving
SIMHA MUKHI: Lion-face
SITA PRIYA: One who is dear to Sita
SOBALI: Name of Ghandari, wife of Dhrtarastra
SOMILAKA: Placid
SUBHADRA: Sister of Lord Krsna
SUCHIMUKHA: Needle-like face
SUMANAS: The moon
SUNANDA: Great pleasure; very happy
SUVARANASIDDHI: Gift of gold
SYAMALA: black; dark blue
SYENA: Beautiful
TIRYAK TILAKA: With a tilaka mark that is curved, oblique or
                                horizontal.
VAKRANASA: Crooked nose
VYAGHRA: Strong like a lion
YUMUNA: River Yamuna in India (dark colour)

THE BENEFITS OF COW URINE AND COW DUNG

The urine of a cow is salty, and according to Ayur-Vedic medicine the cow's urine is very effective in treating patients suffering from liver trouble.

SB 3.2.8. purport

Even in the material world, cow dung is accepted as purified and antiseptic. A person can keep stacks of cow dung in one place, and it will not create a bad odour to disturb anyone.

SB 5.3.33 puport

Nobody would walk by a heap of human stool but we do not mind cow stool.

BG lect. 1972 SP

The cows delivered five products, namely milk, yoghurt, ghee, urine and cow dung..... Panca gavya, the five products received from the cow, namely milk, yoghurt, ghee, cow dung and cow urine are required in all ritualistic ceremonies performed according to Vedic directions. Cow urine and cow dung are uncontaminated, and since even the urine and dung of a cow are important, we can just imagine how important this animal is for human civilization.

SB 8.8.11 purport

Mother Yasoda, Rohini, and other elderly gopis immediately performed the auspicious rituals by taking the tail of a cow and circumambulating His body. The child was completely washed with the urine of a cow, and the dust created by the hooves of the cows was thrown all over His body. This incident gives us a clear indication of how important the cow is to the family, society and to living beings in general. The transcendental body of Krishna did not require any protection, but to instruct us on the importance of the cow, the Lord was smeared over with cow dung, washed with urine of a cow, and sprinkled with the dust upraised by the walking of the cows.

KB Ch.6 para 9

In the Ayur-Veda, cow dung dried and burned to ashes is used as a tooth powder.

SP BG Lect. 1968

In India, cow dung is accepted as pure, and yet cow dung is the stool of an animal. In one place you'll find the Vedic injunction that if you touch stool, you have to take a bath immediately. But in another place it is said that the stool of a cow is pure. If you smear cow dung in an impure place that place becomes pure.... In Calcutta, a very prominent scientist and doctor analyzed cow dung and found that it contains all antiseptic properties.

Sri Isopanisad intro

The benefits of cow dung are well-known throughout the agricultural world, being highly prized for its fertilizing and soil building properties. Other common uses are as follows:

1. As Fuel.
   The cow dung is made into round patties and allowed to dry out. It is often stacked and covered to be used when required. The dried dung is then simply put into the fire where it burns very well.

2. As a source of gas.
   The manure is stored in an enclosed covered vessel where by the process of decomposition a burnable gas is given off. This gas can be stored and used as fuel.

3. As a wall and floor cleaner.
   In hot countries the dung can be mixed with water and used as a paste for spreading on walls and floors. The result is a hard surface which can be kept clean. Also flies do not like to stay on it for very long.

Govinda jaya jaya
Gopala jaya jaya
Radha-ramana hari
Govinda jaya jaya

A SELECTION OF QUOTES ABOUT COWS

I can be worshipped within the cows by offerings of grass and other suitable grains and paraphernalia for the pleasure and health of the cows.   SB 11.11.43

In his childhood, the Almighty Lord was surrounded by cowherd boys and calves, and thus He travelled on the shore of the Yamuna river, through gardens densely covered with trees and filled with vibrations of chirping birds.   SB 3.2.27

Although the cow is beneficial because one can draw religious principles from her.... For a Sanatanist (a follower of Vedic principles), it is the duty of every householder to have cows and bulls as household paraphernalia, not only for drinking milk but also for deriving religious principles. The Sanatanist worships cows on religious principles and respects brahmanas. The cow's milk is required for the sacrificial fire, and by performing sacrifices the householder can be happy. The cow's calf is not only beautiful to look at, but also gives satisfaction to the cow, and so she delivers as much milk as possible.   SB 1.17.3 purport

His ((Krishna's) next duty was to give cows in charity to the brahmanas. Lord Krishna used to give as many as 13,084 cows. Each of them was decorated with a silken cover and pearl necklace, their horns were covered with gold plating, and their hooves were silver-plated. All of them were full of milk, due to having their first-born calves with them, and they were very tame and peaceful.... The Lord is generally known as Go brahmana hitaya ca, which means that His first duty is to see to the welfare of the cows and the brahmanas. Thus He used to give the cows in charity to the brahmanas, with opulent decorations and paraphernalia. Then wishing for the welfare of all living entities, He would touch auspicious articles such as milk, honey, ghee, gold, jewels and fire.... After decorating Himself in this way, the Lord would then look at marble statues of the cow and calf.
KB Ch.69 para 10

Lord Krishna would offer obeisances to the cows.
SB 10.70.10

The cows appeared to be tired from standing with their heavy milk bags. By sitting and chewing grass, they became happy, and Krishna was pleased to see them.

KB Ch.20 para 17

While herding the very beautiful bulls and cows, the Lord, who was the reservoir of all opulence and fortunes, used to blow His flute and thus He enlivened His faithful followers, the cowherd boys.

It is mentioned herein that the beautiful cows and bulls were of various checkered colours - red, black, green, yellow, ash etc. And because of their colours and healthy smiling features, the atmosphere was enlivening.

SB 3.2.29 purport

During the reign of Maharaja Yudhisthira, the clouds showered all the water that people needed, and the earth produced all the necessities of man in profusion. Due to its fatty milk bag and cheerful attitude, the cow used to moisten the grazing ground with milk.

It is said here that the cows used to moisten the pasturing land with milk because their milk bags were fatty and the animals were joyful. Do they not require, therefore, proper protection for a joyful life by being fed with a sufficient quantity of grass in the field?

SB 1.10.4 purport

The bull is the emblem of the moral principle and the cow is the representative of the earth. When the bull and cow are in a joyful mood, it is to be understood that the people of the world are also in a joyful mood. The reason is that the bull helps production of grains in the agricultural field, and the cow delivers milk, the miracle of aggregate food values. The human society, therefore, maintains these two important animals very carefully so that they can wander everywhere in cheerfulness.

SB 1.16.18 purport

The Supreme Personality of Godhead said... The brahmanas, the cows and defenceless creatures are My own body.

SB 3.16.10

Better to keep cowshed vacant than have a troublesome cow.

Bengali Proverb

All of the boys were fearing that their very means of livelihood, the cows, were now lost.

KB Ch.19 para 1

The cow, for instance, gives milk, but she does not drink that milk, she eats grass and grain, and her milk is designated as food for human beings. Such is the arrangement of the Supreme Lord.

Iso Mantra 1

Sometimes the naughty babies (Krishna and Balarama) would crawl up to the cowshed, catch the tail of a calf and stand up. The calves being disturbed, would immediately begin running here and there, and the children would be dragged over clay and cowdung.

KB Ch.8 para 11

One should gently scratch the body of a cow, offer her a mouthful of green grass and reverentially circumambulate her. If cows are maintained nicely and comfortably, Lord Gopala will be pleased.

Gautamiya Tantra

It is very important to note in this connection how wealthy the inhabitants of Vrindavana were simply by raising cows. All the cowherd men belonged to the vaisya community, and their business was to protect the cows and cultivate crops. By their dress and ornaments, and by their behaviour, it appears that although they were in a small village, they still were rich in natural possessions. They possessed such an abundance of various kinds of milk products that they were throwing butter lavishly on each other's bodies without restriction in celebration of Lord Krishna's birth ceremony. Their wealth was in milk, yoghurt, clarified butter and many other milk products, and by trading their agricultural products, they were rich in various kinds of jewelry, ornaments and costly dresses. Not only did they possess these things, but they could give them away in charity, as did Nanda Maharaja,

KB Ch.5 para 8

WHEN COWS ARE NOT PROTECTED

Once, when Maharaja Pariksit was on his way to conquer the world, he saw the master of Kali-yuga, who was lower than a sudra, disguised as a king and hurting the legs of a cow and bull. The King at once caught hold of him to deal sufficient punishment.
SB 1.16.4

Cow killers are condemned to rot in hellish life for as many thousands of years as there are hairs on the body of the cow.
CC Adi Lila 17.106

But in Kali Yuga, (the present age), the calves are separated fom the cows as early as possible for purposes which may not be mentioned in these pages of Srimad Bhagavatam. The cow stands with tears in her eyes, the sudra milkman draws milk from the cow artificially, and when there is no milk the cow is sent to be slaughtered. These greatly sinful acts are responsible for all the troubles in present society. People do not know what they are doing in the name of economic development. The influence of this age will keep them in the darkness of ignorance. Despite all endeavours for peace and prosperity, they must try to see the cows and the bulls happy in all respects. Foolish people do not know how one earns happiness by making the cows and bulls happy, but it is a fact by the law of nature.
SB 1.17.3 purport

Every living creature is the son of the Supreme Lord, and He does not tolerate even an ant being killed. One has to pay for it. So, indulgence in animal killing for the taste of the tongue is the grossest kind of ignorance. A human being has no need to kill animals because God has supplied so many nice things. If one indulges in meat-eating anyway, it is to be understood that he is acting in ignorance and is making his future very dark. Of all kinds of animal killing, the killing of cows is most vicious because the cow gives us all kinds of pleasure by supplying milk. Cow slaughter is an act of the grossest type of ignorance.
BG 14.16 purport

To kill cows means to end human civilization
SB 1.4.9 purport.

Lord Krishna as Govinda is more inclined to the brahmanas and the cows, indicating thereby that human prosperity depends more on these two items, namely brahmanical culture and cow protection. Lord Krishna is never satisfied where these are lacking.

SB 1.8.22 purport

Cow not killed in any circumstances. SB 10.1.37

Cows and bulls should be protected in all circumstances and never harmed in any way or else there will be serious troubles in society, as we can witness in our present times.

FROM BULLS TO OXEN

Padmagandha and Pisangaksa are Krishna's pet oxen.
LRKGDD 110

In the practical application of the symbiotic relationship between cows and men, one is required to castrate most of the bulls. The bulls which are not being kept specifically for impregnating the cows can be castrated and thus made more useful as draught animals. Uncastrated bulls are not generally suitable for draught work.

The castration of bulls and the piercing of their noses are two important elements of the interdependent relationship, by which man can control and work the oxen.

Looking at history one will find ample evidence showing that the castration of bulls has always been an aspect of male bovine husbandry. In modern-day India it is an accepted practice that working bulls are castrated and bulls for breeding are set free and not worked.

There is a certain amount of practical Vedic evidence regarding castration which I personally accept and therefore have included it in this book. Such practical information is commonly accepted by farmers throughout the world, who use castration for their own cattle management purposes.

Temperament

It is an undisputed fact that the temperament of a full uncastrated bull is much different to that of an ox, steer or bullock, (a castrated bull). A breeding bull is required to be a strong passionate individual who readily impregnates cows. An entire bull is always on the hunt for cows which are ready to mate. These bulls are generally fiery by nature and potentially dangerous. Bulls from dairy breeds are notorious for their bad temper. Infact in the United Kingdom you are not permitted to have dairy bulls running with cows where people are walking. Friesian and Jersey entire males are especially well known for their vicious nature.

To attempt to train such fiery individuals for work would be both dangerous and difficult. There are however, exceptions to this rule. In the Krsna Balarama Goshalla in Vrndavan the use of uncastrated bulls for some work is common practice.

I understand that such a policy is frowned upon by the local residents. The working of entire males is certainly not a general practice in India. Some breeds of Indian cattle are very docile, even the bulls. They have a different nature to the western bulls. It would be difficult to train uncastrated western bulls and other bulls from the third world.

When a bull is castrated it becomes quieter by nature and its stature also changes. To train oxen is relatively easy and manageable.

Do be aware that castrating a bull is no guarantee of it becoming docile. My experience at Bhaktivedanta Manor has shown that some breeds are potentially untrustworthy even as oxen. Friesians often fall into this category. On the other hand I have found our Kerry oxen are all generally good-natured and docile.

Controlled breeding

Castrating a bull which is not required for impregnation ensures a controlled breeding programme. A potent bull must be carefully selected and allowed freedom to roam, at least that is the ancient Vedic model. Bulls which are not suitable for procreation can find useful employment as working oxen. Castrating unsuitable bulls prevents them from fathering unsuitable offspring.

How and when to castrate

One should not castrate a bull too soon or it's growth will be affected. Neither should it be done too late as the temperament will not change.

The right time for castration is between eight months and three years. I would advise that western bulls should not be left much after one year as they often have a harsher temperament. In India the bulls are castrated between one and three years, being more docile by nature.

Castration may be carried out in a variety of ways depending on local tradition. However one should use a professional veterinarian to perform the actual operation. Such an important part of a bulls anatomy cannot be left to unqualified hands. In many countries, once the bull calf has reached a certain age it can only be castrated by a qualified vet.

Jaya and Dharma - two of the working oxen at Bhaktivedanta Manor, UK

Jaya at rest

HARNESSING A BULL THROUGH ITS NOSE

As a cow, bound through the nose by a long rope, is conditioned.
SB 1.13.42

By subduing seven bulls whose noses were not pierced.
SB 3.3.4

Just as a bull, prompted by a rope in its nose, is controlled by its owner.
SB 3.15.8

Like bulls obliged to move according to the direction of a driver pulling on ropes knotted to their noses.
SB 5.1.14

The entire world is controlled by Him just as a bull is controlled by a rope in its nose.
SB 6.3.12

He immediately divided Himself into seven Krishnas, and each one of Them immediately caught hold of a bull and bridled its nose, thus bringing it under control as if it were a plaything.
KB Ch.57 para 22

No question of independence, a horse or a bull is bound by its nose and the driver, as he pushes and pulls on the rope it has to go according to that.
SB Lect. Toronto 1976

These quotes allow us a glimpse of a very practical though perhaps controversial demonstration of the God-given symbiotic relationship between man and bull. From these references one can see that to pierce a bull's nose and harness it for work is a natural and authorised method of male bovine husbandry.

Moving a bull by its nose

A western bull can weigh up to 1500 kgs. On average a dairy bull will weigh between 800-1000 kgs. Any bull, tethered through its nose by using either a nose-ring (western style) or a rope (third world style) can be controlled and made to move according to the herdsman's wishes, within reason. One bull I know would not enter a horse box even though he was being pulled by the nose and tapped on the rump. In most cases though a bull will submit to the pulling on his nose. Thereby a 75kg man can control two oxen weighing 1500-3000 kgs between them.

The correct age to pierce the nose

As yet I have found no sastric evidence which suggests the correct age for piercing a bulls nose. Experience tells me that the appropriate time is when the young bull has sufficient strength to overpower its handler. In western breed cattle, I estimate the age of one year to be about right. The nose piercing must be carried out by a proficient, qualified and experienced person. Mistakes can cause unnecessary suffering and discomfort for the bull. There is even the risk of a fatality if this task is not carried out correctly.

As a person who has recently had their ears or nose pierced will be very conscious of the presence of a ring or stud, so too will the newly-pierced bull be aware of the ring or rope in his nose. After piercing, one should be extremely considerate when handling the bull by the nose. Within a short while, the only time that he will be aware of his ring will be when he is prompted by the driver.

How to harness the nose

1.   Indian Style.
       To harness a bull that has a rope through its nose, in the
       Indian fashion is very simple as this rope is permanently
       positioned around the head as well as going through the
       nose. To affix a driving rope to the bull, it is simply a
       matter of attaching another rope to the permanent 'nose
       rope' at the middle of the back of the bulls head.

INDIAN NOSE ROPE

2.   Western Style.

The western method of harnessing (see page 73) is slightly different due to the fact that the bulls have a nose ring and there is no rope fixed permanently around the bulls head. For this reason, you will require the following equipment:

*   A small linked chain or a rope about one metre in length for each bull. A small hook should be attached to both ends.

*   A length of rope about 6 metres long.

Thread one end of the chain (or short rope) through the nose-ring and secure it back on itself. The chain (or rope) should then be brought up one side of the bull's face, around the back of the ears, over the back of the neck and down the other side of the face, towards the nose, threading through the other side of the nose-ring. Again, the free end should be secured back on itself. What you have created is a similar arrangement to the Indian nose-rope. The only difference being that the chains (or rope) can be detached.

Whether you use chain or rope, it should not be be put on too tightly as this will cause discomfort and confusion to the bull who will feel a constant pulling on his nose and consequently prove reluctant to move forward.

Once the chain has been secured around the head and through the nose-ring, the harness rope can be attached. This can tied or   secured by using a hook or clip. As with the Indian system, it must be secured to the chain at the central point at the back of the head

The attitude of the driver.

The attitude of the handler should be a combination of friendliness and firmness. He should be very affectionate towards his oxen but as he has to dominate them he must also be firm.
At the outset, it may be hard to get the required response from one's oxen, therefore one must remain patient and tolerant.

To drive a pair of oxen, the system is quite simple.

Commands for driving

The commands used as an example in this book are very simple. They are commonly used by American Ox Teams and I have adopted them for my own use. Should you prefer, your own words or those commonly used in your area can be adopted for driving your oxen. Whatever you decide, to avoid confusing the bull,the words you use should be short and sound different to each other.

Starting off
Call **"Get up"**, and at the same time tap both bulls on the rump with a stick. This should set them both off walking. If they stop or slow down unnecessarily, repeat the same procedure.

Stopping
To stop, call **"Whoa"**, pull back on both ropes. Both bulls should stop. When pulling back on the ropes try to keep them straight and not pull to the left or right as this might cause one of the bulls to turn unnecessarily.

Of all commands **"Whoa"** is the most important. For safety reasons "whoa" means stopping dead, not a step further. When you want to slow down, use another term like **"Steady"**.

Turning left
Call **"Haw"**, then pull the left rope connected to the nose of the left bull, simultaneously tap the rump of the right bull. The left bull will slow down or stop while the right bull will continue to walk on and thus turn around the left bull until both oxen are facing left.

Turning right
Call **"Gee"**, then pull the right rope connected to the nose of the right bull, simultaneously tap the rump of the left bull. The right bull will slow down or stop while the left bull will continue to walk on and thus turn around the right bull until both oxen are facing right.

Moving backwards
To move the oxen back, call **"Back"**, then pull back on both ropes until the animals start to walk backwards. Keep the pressure on the nose-ropes until you have reversed the oxen the required distance.

You may not be able to travel very far backwards with your team. There may be the tendency for the oxen to split apart from each other. This can be overcome by tying them together by the rumps.

From training to working

The above mentioned system can be successfully employed in training your oxen. Indeed the method described is relevant both for bulls in training and fully trained bulls.

At the outset, the oxen will be unsteady and unsure, even somewhat nervous. With firm but gentle handling accompanied by a regulated training and working schedule your oxen will very quickly settle down.

From training to working
The Author with two of the oxen at Bhaktivedanta Manor (top)
Ploughing Demonstration during an Ox Power Open Day (bottom)

If the trainer has not had any previous experience of working with oxen, the following points should be appreciated. At first the oxen will be quite nervous of many things, from putting on the yoke; the feeling of being trapped by it; the tugging on their noses; the closeness of another ox at the other end of the yoke, (who may want to butt him): to the pulling of a load etc.. The trainer must be prepared for the oxen to be somewhat unpredictable and for this reason great patience and kindness should be shown towards them. They will undoubtedly make many mistakes at first, so one should be prepared and at the same time, willing to persevere.

The right age for training

The younger you can get your oxen used to being led around by a rope the better. In fact walking your young, or un-broken oxen around can be part of their training, in that it gets them used to man and to being controlled.

It should be noted that oxen cannot start serious work, like ploughing or hauling loads until they are three years or older.

The Training Schedule

If the oxen are used to being led, the training will be somewhat easier.

Assuming though that they have never been yoked, the training programme could follow these lines:

Days 1-3
Secure both oxen to a hitching rail and put on the yoke securely. Leave the oxen there for about 1-2 hours each day.

Days 4-10
Attach a log to the yoke and proceed to drive the team around a large field or open space using the commands previously mentioned.

Day 11 onwards
Gradually begin to do some farm work such as pulling carts, harrowing,weeding etc.

Training your oxen to plough will take the most time as it involves one ox walking along a furrow in a straight line. With practice, it will come for sure.

Pulling a log or a small hitch-cart

To make driving the oxen a little easier, give them something to pull. If you use a log, it should not be too light. If it is too heavy the untrained oxen will back off from pulling.

One system which works very well is to attach the yoke to a hitch-cart (basically, two wheels, a seat, a pole and a hitching pin) and then attach a log or a chain harrow to the back. You can ride on the cart and drive the oxen from your seat from the first day out. There is the added benefit of having a lot of control over the oxen from this position.

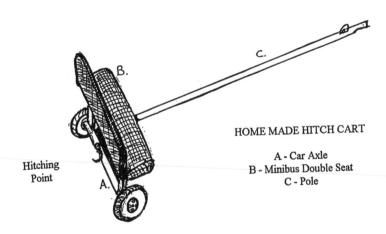

HOME MADE HITCH CART

A - Car Axle
B - Minibus Double Seat
C - Pole

Hitching Point

Bringing in the hay at Bhaktivedanta Manor, UK.

The wonder of nasal harnessing

As already discussed on page 75, this wonderful natural system will enable you to do some farm work quite quickly. The important work of ploughing may take a few weeks to learn properly.

Putting a trained ox with an ox in training

If you can put your untrained ox alongside a fully trained ox on the yoke then the training will be less traumatic and easier. The less experienced ox will follow its partner.

Cows and draught work

Barren cows, heifers or any other category of cow must not be used for draught work. From scriptural evidence cited throughout this book, such a thing as working cows is forbidden. The duty of a cow is to produce offspring and give milk. It is strictly the bull's duty to work.

Regular work lessens the need for nasal prompting

With regular use, you may find that gradually your voice will be sufficient to get the team of oxen to do what you want. Rather, they will be so well used, that voice commands will generally be adequate for most work. Some oxen however may always require the use of ropes and physical reminders.

Gentle persuasion

Any verbal or physical correction your oxen may need should be done with the greatest respect and control. Rebuking out of anger or frustration should not be entertained and will only complicate the working relationship between man and animal.

Different training methods

Should you wish to learn more about the numerous methods of training working oxen, there are many excellent publications available on the market. The instructions in this book have purposely addressed the system of working bulls by the harnessing of their noses, as described in the opening verses of this chapter.

How many hours can the oxen work?

A pair of oxen who are worked regularly should be able to plough an acre a day (0.4 hectare), which is about eight hours work. If you are working with newly trained oxen then the number of hours they work should be increased gradually. To become very strong, they will need good food and regular work.

Feeding working oxen

The quantities of extra food, in the form of grains for the bulls depends on the type of work they are doing. A guide to feeding appears in Chapter Four.

When bulls are yoked together and tied to a central post to thresh rice, they tread round that pivot without deviating from their proper positions - one bull being closest to the post, another in the middle, and a third on the outside.

SB 5.23.3

Yokes

There are numerous types of yoke used throughout the world; indeed practically every region has its own favoured design. Yoke size and shape will be dependant on the breed of the oxen who will carry it and also whether such oxen have humps (Asian and African) or not (Western /Northern).

A typical Indian yoke is simply a bamboo pole which is pushed by the humps of the oxen. It is very simple and easy to make.

The basic requirements of a yoke are:

- It should be comfortable for the bulls

- It must be strong enough to do the work prescribed

- It should be easy to put on and take off

- Preferably it will last a long time

- It is made from local materials

The yoke shown on the following page has been, and still is used considerably at Bhaktivedanta Manor, England. In practice, this yoke is suitable for all work except ploughing for which a narrower yoke should be employed - allowing 18-20" between the U bars rather than 26". The wood used is hickory, although Ash would have been as suitable.

The wood was bought from a local timber merchant as a cut piece 7 ins x 4ins x 54 ins. The semi-circular neck pieces were cut out using a cross saw and the holes made using a wood drill. The general areas of the wood were then planed and the neck pieces sanded and smoothed.

The U bars were fashioned by a local metal engineer who bent the metal to shape and also drilled the metal holes for the R clips (the pieces which hold the bars in place and alter their height).

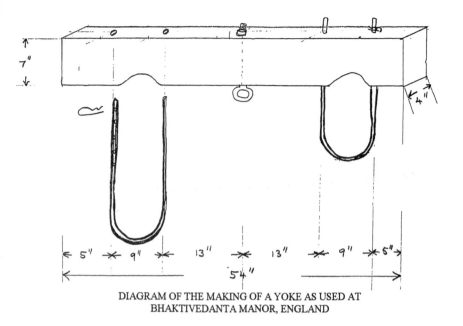

DIAGRAM OF THE MAKING OF A YOKE AS USED AT
BHAKTIVEDANTA MANOR, ENGLAND

Different types of yoke

The following are a selection of the many types of yokes used throughout the world.

1.   America/Australia

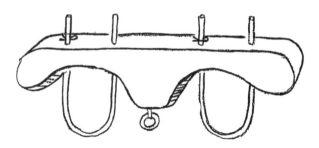

2.   Pakistan

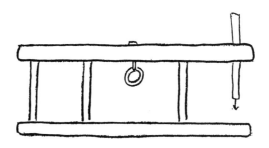

3.   Afghanistan

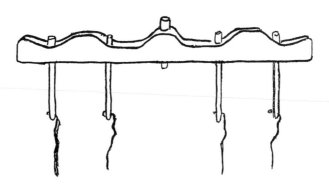

THE MANU SAMHITA AND COWS

Let a brahmana not step over a rope to which a calf has been tied.
MS 4.38

Let him pass by a mound of earth, a cow, a deity, a brahmana, clarified butter, honey, a crossway and well-known trees, turning his right hand towards them.
MS 4.39

Let him not void urine on a road, on ashes or in a cowpen....nor on ploughed land.
MS 4.45 & 46

The intellect of a man who voids urine against...a cow...perishes.
MS 4.52

Let him not interrupt a cow who is suckling her calf, nor tell anybody of it.
MS 4.59

Let him not travel with untrained beasts of burden, nor with animals that are tormented by hunger or disease, or whose horns, eyes, or hooves have been injured, or whose tails have been disfigured.
MS 4.67

Let him always travel with beasts which are well broken in, swift, endowed with lucky marks, and perfect in colour and form, without urging them much with the goad.
MS 4.68

To ride on the back of cows or of oxen is anyhow a blamable act.
MS 4.72

A brahmana should not study in the cow-pen.
MS 4.116

Let a brahmana never accept food at which a cow has smelt.
MS 4.209

A giver of a draught-ox obtains great good fortune, a giver of a cow, the world of the sun.

MS 4.231

A brahmana should carefully avoid the thickened milk of a cow (colostrum, obtained just after a calf is born).

MS 5.6

A brahmana should avoid the milk of a cow or other animal within ten days after her calving... of a cow in heat, or of one that has no calf with her.

MS 5.8

A vaisya becomes pure by touching his goad or the nose-string of his oxen.

MS 5.99

Smearing with cow-dung is a purifier.

MS 5.105

Land is purified by sweeping, by smearing it with cow-dung, by sprinkling it with cows urine or milk, by scraping and by cows staying on it during a day and night.

MS 5.124

Food which has been smelt by cows becomes pure by scattering earth over it.

MS 5.125

A calf is pure on the flowing of the milk.

MS 5.130

Flies, a cow, a horse.... are pure to the touch.

MS 5.133

During the day the responsibility for the safety of the cattle rests on the herdsman, during the night on the owner, provided they are in his house; if it be otherwise, the herdsman will be responsible for them also during the night.

MS 5.230

A vaisya becomes pure by touching his goad or the nose-string of his oxen.

MS 5.99

The hired herdsman who is paid with milk, may milk with the consent of the owner the best cow out of ten; such shall be his hire if no other wages are paid.

MS 8.231

The herdsman alone shall make good the loss of a beast strayed, destroyed by snakes, killed by dogs (or other wild beasts), or by falling into a pit, if he did not duly exert himself to prevent it.

MS 8.232

But for an animal stolen by thieves, though he raised an alarm, the herdsman shall not pay, provided he gives notice to his master at the proper place and time.

MS 8.233

If cattle die, let him carry to his master their ears, skin, tails, bladders, tendons, and the yellow concrete bile, and let him point out their particular marks.

MS 8.234

But if they, kept in proper order, graze together in the forest, and a wolf, suddenly jumping on one of them kills it, the herdsman shall bear in that case no responsibilty.

MS 8.236

On all sides of a village a space one hundred dhanus (600 feet) or three samya throws in breadth shall be reserved for pasture, and thrice that space round a town.

MS 8.237

If the cattle do damage to unfenced crops on that common, the king shall in that case not punish the herdsman.

MS 8.238

The owner of the field shall make there a hedge over which a camel cannot look, and stop every gap through which a dog or a boar can thrust its head.

MS 8.239

If cattle do mischief in an enclosed field near a highway or near a village, the herdsman shall be fined one hundred panas; but cattle unattended by a herdsman, the watchman in the field shall drive away.

MS 8.240

For damage in other fields each head of cattle shall pay a fine of one pana and a quarter, and in all cases the value of the crop destroyed shall be made good to the owner of the field; that is the settled rule.

MS 8.241

But Manu has declared that no fine shall be paid for damage done by a cow within ten days after her calving, by bulls (those set at liberty to roam) and by cattle sacred to the Gods (cows dedicated to Temples) whether they are attended by the herdsman or not.

MS 8.242

If the crops are destroyed by the husbandman's (farmer/grower) own fault (i.e. he let the cows eat his crops or else the field has not been sown in the proper time) the fine shall amount to ten times as much as the king's share, but the fine shall be only half that amount if the fault lay with the servants and the farmer had no knowledge of it.

MS 8.243

They declare with respect to a carriage, its driver and its owner that there are ten cases in which no punishment for damage done can be inflicted, in other cases a fine is presented:

When the nose-string is snapped, when the yoke is broken, when the carriage turns sideways or back (due to bad roads or startled animals), when the axle or a wheel is broken.

When the leather thongs, the rope around the neck of the bridle are broken, and when the driver has loudly called out 'Make way" Manu has declared that in all these cases no punishments shall be inflicted.

But if the cart turns off the road through the driver's want of skill, the owner shall be fined if damage is done, 200 panas.

If the driver is skillful but negligent, he alone shall be fined, if the driver is unskilled, the occupants of the carriage also shall be fined 100 panas.

But if he is stopped on his way by cattle or by another carriage and he caused the death of any living being a fine shall without doubt be imposed.

MS 8.290-295

The taking of roots and of fruit from trees, of wood for a sacrificial fire, and of grass for feeding cows, Manu has declared not to be theft.

MS 8.339

He who ties up unbound or sets free tied up cattle of other men... shall have uncured the guilt of a thief.

MS 8.342

After a vaisya has received the sacraments and has taken a wife he shall be always attentive to the business whereby he may subsist and to that of tending cattle.

MS 9.326

A vaisya must never conceive of not keeping cattle.

MS 9.328

He who has committed a minor offence by slaying a cow or bull shall drink during the first month a decoction of barley grains, having shaved all his hair, and covering himself with the hide of the slain cow he must live in a cow-house.

During the following two months he shall eat a small quantity of food without any factitious salt at every fourth meal-time and shall bathe in the urine of cows, keeping his organs under control.

During the day he shall follow the cows and standing upright, inhale the dust raised by their hooves; at night after serving and worshipping them, he shall remain in a posture called virasana.

Controlling himself and free from anger he must stand when they stand, follow them when they walk and seat himself when they lie down.

When a cow is sick or is threatened by danger from thieves, tigers and the like, or falls, or sticks in a morass, he must relieve her by all possible means.

In heat, in rain, or in cold, or when the wind blows violently, he must not seek to shelter himself, without first sheltering the cows according to his ability.

Let him not say a word if a cow eats anything in his own or another's house or field or in the threshing floor, or if a calf drinks milk.

The slayer of a cow who serves cows in this manner removes after three months the guilt which he incurred by killing a cow.

But after he has fully performed the penance he must give to brahmanas learned in the Veda 10 cows and 1 bull, or if he does not possess so much property he must offer to them all he has.

MS 11.109-117

KAUTILYA'S ARTHASASTRA

The Superintendent of Cows

The superintendent of cows shall supervise:

1. *herds maintained for wages - vetanopagrahikam;*
2. *herds surrendered for a fixed amount of dairy produce - karapratkara;*
3. *useless and abandoned herds - bhagnotsrshtakam;*
4. *herds maintained for a share of dairy produce - bhaganupravishtam;*
5. *classes of herds - vrajaparyagram;*
6. *cattle that strayed - nashtam*
7. *cattle that are irrecoverably lost - vinahtam;*
8. *the amassed quantity of milk and clarified butter.*

1. *When a cowherd, a buffalo herdsman, a milker, a churner and a hunter (one who guards the cows against wild animals), fed by wages, graze milk-cows in hundreds, for if they graze the herds for the profit of milk and ghee, they will starve the calves to death; that system of rearing cattle is termed "herds maintained for wages".*

2. *When a single person rears a hundred heads made up of equal numbers of each of aged cows, milk-cows, pregnant cows, heifers and calves and gives to the owner 8 varakas of clarified butter per annum, as well as the branded skin of dead cows if any, that system is called " herds surrendered for a fixed amount of dairy produce".*

3. *When those who rear a hundred heads made up of equal numbers of each of afflicted cattle, crippled cattle, cattle that cannot be milked by anyone but the accustomed person, cattle that kill their own calves, give in return to the owner a share in dairy produce it is termed " useless and abandoned herd".*

4. *When under the fear of cattle-lifting enemies, cattle are kept under the care of the superintendent, giving him one-tenth of the dairy produce for his protection, it is termed "herds maintained for a share in dairy produce".*

5.   When the superintendent classifies cattle as calves, steers, tameable ones, draught oxen, bulls that are to be trained to yoke, bulls kept for crossing cows, buffaloes and draught buffaloes; female calves, male steers, heifers, pregnant cows, milk-cattle, barren cattle - either cows or buffaloes; calves that are a month or two old as well as those which are still younger and when, as he ought to, he brands them all, inclusive of their calves of one or two months old along with those stray cattle which have remained unclaimed in the herds for a month or two; and when he registers the branded marks, natural marks, colour and the distance from one horn to another of each of the cattle, that system is known as "class of herds".

6.   When an animal is carried off by thieves or finds itself into the herds of others or strays unknown, it is called "lost".

7.   When an animal is entangled in a quagmire or precipice or dies of disease or of old age, or drowned in water; or when it is killed by the fell of a tree or off a river bank, or it is beaten to death with a staff or a stone, or is struck by lightning, or is devoured by a tiger or bitten by a cobra, or is carried off by a crocodile, or is involved in the midst of a forest fire, it is termed " irrecoverably lost".

Cowherds shall endeavour to keep them away from such dangers.

When a person substitutes an animal bearing the royal band mark for a private one, he shall be punished with the first amercement.

When a person recovers a local cattle from thieves, he shall receive the promised reward; and when a man rescues a foreign cattle from thieves, he shall receive half its value.

Cowherds shall apply remedies to calves or aged cows or cows suffering from disease.

They shall graze the herds in forests which are severally allotted as pasture grounds for various seasons and from which thieves, tigers and other molesting beasts are driven away by hunters aided by their hounds.

With a view to scare out snakes and tigers and as a definite means of knowing the whereabouts of herds, sounding bells shall be attached to the neck of timid cattle.

Cowherds shall allow their cattle to enter into such rivers or lakes as are of equal depth all round broad, and free from mire and crocodiles and shall protect them from dangers under such circumstances.

Whenever an animal is caught hold of by a thief, a tiger, a snake, or a crocodile, or when it is too infirm owing to age or disease, they shall make a report of it; otherwise they shall be compelled to make good the loss.

When an animal dies a natural death, they shall surrender the skin with the brand mark, if it is a cow or a buffalo; the skin together with the ear, if it is a goat or sheep; the tail with the skin containing the brand mark, if it is an ass or a camel; the skin if it is a young one; besides the above they shall also restore the fat, bile, sinew, teeth, hooves, horns, and bones,

They (the cowherds) may sell either flesh or dried flesh.

They shall give buttermilk as drink to dogs and hogs, and reserve a little in a bronze vessel to prepare their own dish; they may also make use of coagulated milk or cheese to render their oil-cakes relishable.

He who sells his cow from among the herds shall pay to the king one-fourth the value of the cow.

If he allows the time of milking to lapse, he shall forfeit the profit thereof (i.e. the milk).

The same rule shall hold good in case of negligence of the opportune moment for putting a string through the nose of a bull and other animals, and for taming or training them to the yoke.

One drona of a cow's milk will, when churned, yield one prastha of butter; the same quantity of a buffaloes milk will yield one- seventh prastha more; and the same quantity of milk of goats and sheep will produce one-half prastha more.

In all kinds of milk, the exact quantity of butter shall be ascertained by churning; for increase in the supply of milk and butter depends on the nature of the soil and quantity and quality of fodder and water.

When a person causes a bull attached to a herd to fight with another bull, he shall be punished with the first amercement; when a bull is injured under such circumstances, he shall be punished with the highest amercement.

Cattle shall be grouped in herds of ten each of similar colour while they are being grazed.

According to the protective strength of the cowherds and the capacity of the cattle to go far and wide to graze, cowherds shall take their cattle either far or near.

Once in six months, sheep and other animals shall be shorn of their wool.
The same rules shall apply to herds of horses, asses, camels and hogs.

For bulls which are provided with nose-strings, and which equal horses in speed and in carrying loads, half a bhara of meadow grass, twice the above quantity of ordininary grass, 1 tula (100 palas) of oil cakes, 10 adhakas of bran, 5 palas of salt, 1 kudumba of oil for rubbing over the nose, 1 prastha of drink, 1 adhaka of curds, 1 drona of barley or cooked masha, 1 drona of milk; or half an adhaka of sura, 1 prastha of oil or ghee, 10 palas of sugar or jaggery, 1 pala of the fruit of sringiberi (ginger) may be substituted for milk

The same commodities_less by one quarter each will form the diet for mules, cows and asses; twice the quantity of the above things for buffaloes and camels.

Draught oxen and cows supplying milk shall be provided subsistence in proportion to the duration of time the oxen are kept at work, and the quantity of milk which the cows supply.

All cattle shall be supplied with abundance of fodder and water.

Thus the manner of rearing herds of cattle has been dealt with. A herd of 100 heads of asses and mules shall contain five male animals; that of goats and and sheep 10; and a herd of ten heads of either cows or buffaloes shall contain 4 male animals.

Thus ends chapter 29 "The Superintendent of Cows" in book 2, "The duties of Government Superintendents" of the Arthasastra of Kautilya.

BRAHMA PURANA AND COWS

They (Krishna and Balarama) grazed the cows in the forest. When they strayed far off into the forest They used to call them by their names. They kept a noose ready on Their shoulders in order to bind the straying cows.

BP 78. 17-18

O dear father (Nanda) we are not agriculturalists. Nor do we sustain ourselves by trading activities. The cows are our deities since we are persons roaming about in the forests.

BP 79.12

Cultivation is the occupation of agriculturalists, trade that of businessmen. To us, cows provide the greatest occupation.

BP 79.15

Let herds of cows with the autumnal flowers adorning their crests go round the mountain (Govardhana) that has been worshipped.

BP 79.23

If one releases a blue-coloured bull..... he obtains heaven.

BP 111.33

Faeces should not be discharged on the path leading to the rural residences, holy centres and fields, nor in a ploughed field, nor in a cowpen.

BP 113.22

One should never disregard or insult brahmanas, fires, cows and the sun.

BP 113.36

One should not look at a cow suckling her calf.

BP 113.102

A plot of land becomes pure by the influence of time, by being burnt, by being swept or when herds of cows pass over it.

BP 113.123

They (Krishna and Balarama) grazed the cows in the forest.
BP 78.17-18

The ground becomes purified by smearing with cow-dung, by scraping, by sprinkling with water.

BP 113.124

The water that gives satisfaction to a cow is pure... Goats and horses are pure in their mouths but not the mouth of cows and calves.

BP 113.130

THE SIVA PURANA

A vaisya shall earn his wealth by means of agriculture and cattle breeding.

SPVS 13.65

Three kinds of sins physical etc are warded off by milk, curd and ghee. The ghee used shall be the one prepared from the milk of a tawny cow.

At the end of the sacrifice monetary gifts shall be given, the preceptor shall be given two cows or a cow and a bull as extra.

SPVS 16.46-48

Namo-gobhyah - obeisances to the cow.

SPVS 20.35

He (Lord Siva) was then seated on the shoulders of the bull.

SPRS 3.47.28

She (a chaste wife) shall never take food without first offering due share to the Gods, the forefathers, the guests, the servants, cows and saintly mendicants.

SPRS 3.53.27

Siva's cowshed is situated there... It is to tend Lord Siva's cows and bulls that he has been ordered by him.

SPRS 5.39.51-52

Riding on a bull is despicable.

SPRS 5.44.53

There was a fine cow tied up in the courtyard.

O great sages on seeing the cow, tethered in the courtyard, not yet milked, the distressed brahmin desirous of milking it told his wife.

In order to milk the cow he called his wife quickly and said "O beloved, the cow is not yet milked". Thus urged she brought the calf. The brahmana desirous of milk tried to tie up the calf to the peg.

SPKS 6.1-4

If a person sees the face of a cow-killer, he shall take full bath in full dress.

SPKS 25.38

Using a bullock cart constantly as a vehicle through wild jungle is sinful.

SPUS 6.9

Cruel persons who beat cows and bulls; supress them; do not feed them properly and let them alone weak and feeble.

Those who ill-treat bullocks with weighty burden; those who make them draw heavily-laden carts; those who do not let them off free for leisure.

Those who do not rear cows and bullocks properly, let them starve; ill-treat them with heavy burdens; do not treat their wounds and bruises are called the killers of cows. They are sure to fall into hell.

The most sinful persons who castrate bulls by squeezing out their scrotum and those who make heifers draw carts are great sinners sure to fall into hell.

SPUS 6.31-34

There are gifts of gold, cows and land, by making these excellent gifts one is liberated from sins.

SPUS 14.3

These things shall be given every day to those who beg for them - viz. oxen, cows, umbrella, cloth, pairs of shoes, drink and food.

SPUS 14.5

There are 10 great gifts. Gold, gingelly seeds, elephants, virgins, servant maid, house, chariot, jewels, the tawny-coloured cow and ordinary cows.

SPUS 14.7

The gift of the cow duly performed is the most excellent. O Vyasa, no other gift is glorified so much as this.

If anyone makes the gift of a tawny cow along with its calf, adorning the horns with gold, the hoofs with silver and endowed with other characteristics and also gives a bell-metal vessel, that cow returns to him in the form of the wish-yielding celestial cow.
O Vyasa, the donor is thus blessed both here and hereafter.

SPUS 14.21-23

Lamps lighted with fragrant ghee from the milk of a tawny cow, accompanied by camphor are excellent.

Pancagavya consisting of sweet milk, curd and ghee all taken from tawny cows is the favourite of Lord Siva for bathing and drinking.

The dung shall be of the cow, tawny in colour. It is commendable if collected as it falls from the cow before it reaches the ground.

If he collects the dung that has already fallen on the ground the upper and lower portion shall be eschewed. The dung shall not be too watery not too solidified nor dried up. It shall not emit a foul smell.

SPVVS 25.54-55

May the bull, the powerful son of Khamadenu....surrounded by five mother cows.

The five mother cows stationed in Lord Siva's region are Nanda, Sunanda, Surabhi, Susila and Sumanas

SPVVS 31.143-144.

At the lake Skandasaras. At places oxen and hostile bulls are butting against the banks.

SPVVS 41.14

FACTS AND FIGURES

Temperature - 39 C/102 F

Pulse per minute - 45 to 50

Breathing rate per minute - 12 to 16

Teeth (Adult) - 8 incisors, 12 pre-molars, 12 molars.
                   There are no incisors on the upper jaw.

Age of heifer at first bulling - 6-14 months

Earliest time for impregnation - 15-18 months

Frequency of Heat - 18-24 days (21 days on average)

Young bulls become sexually active - 7 to 12 months

Age to castrate - about 12 months for Western type bulls
                     1-3 years for Indian type

Age to pierce the nose - About one year old

Manure. - Each cow/bull will produce approximately 3.2 / 6 tonnes
             of manure each year.
             (1.12 cubic metres of manure weighs 1 tonne)

Water. - A cow will consume about 22 litres of water each day
            plus three litres for every litre of milk produced.

REFERENCES

Bengali proverb

BG. Bhagavad Gita*   14.16 purport
© The Bhaktivedanta Book Trust International. Used with permission

BG Lect.*   Bhagavad Gita lecture in 1966, Bhagavad
                      Gita lecture in 1968, Bhagavad Gita
                      lecture in 1972; by Srila Prabhupada.
© The Bhaktivedanta Book Trust International. Used with permission

BP. Brahma Purana.   78.17-18, 79.12, 79.23, 111.33, 113.22,
                          113.36, 113.102, 113.123, 113.124,
                          113.130.

CC. Caitanya Caritamrta.*   Adi Lila 6.14/155, 17.106.
© The Bhaktivedanta Book Trust International. Used with permission
Gautamiya Tantra.

GL. Govinda Lilamrta. 19.23, 19.24, 19.99, 19.100.

Kautilya's Arthasatra.   Chapter 29 "The Superintendent of Cows"
                            in book 2, "The Duties of Government
                            Superintendents" of the Arthasastra of
                            Kautilya.

KB. Krishna Book*.   Chap.5 para 8,   Chap.6 para 9,
                          Chap.8 para 11, Chap.8 para 12,
                          Chap.11 para 10, Chap.11 para 16,
                          Chap. 12 para 1, Chap.13 para 8,
                          Chap.13 para 11, Chap.13 para 12,
                          Chap. 15 para 6, Chap.19 para 1,
                          Chap.20 para 17, Chap.20 para 22,
                          Chap. 21 para 12, Chap.21 para 14,
                          Chap.37 para 12, Chap.37 para 14,
                          Chap.44 para 15, Chap.45 para 10,
                          Chap.57 para 22, Chap 69 para 10.

© The Bhaktivedanta Book Trust International. Used with permission

Life from life*.   6.
© The Bhaktivedanta Book Trust International. Used with permission

Laghu Sri Sri Radha Krsna Ganadesa Dipika. 197

LRKGDD.   Laghu Radha Krishna Ganodesa Dipika
109,110

Matchless Gifts*   4

MS. Manu Samhita   4.38, 4.39, 4.45, 4.46, 4.52, 4.59, 4.67,
4.68, 4.72, 4.116, 4.209, 4.231, 5.40, 5.6,
5.8, 5.99, 5.105, 5.124, 5.125, 5.130,
5.133, 8.230, 8.231, 8.232, 8.233, 8.234,
8.236, 8.237, 8.238, 8.239, 8.240, 8.241,
8.242, 8.243, 8.290-295, 8.325, 8.339,
8.342, 9.326, 9.328, 11.109-117.

PQPA*   Perfect Questions Perfect Answers

Ramayana Bala Kand   36.15

SB Lect.*   Srimad Bhagavatam lecture in 1969,
Srimad Bhagavatam lecture in 1972,
Srimad Bhagavatam Lecture in Toronto in
1976: by Srila Prabhupada.

SB. Srimad Bhagavatam*

1.4.9 purport,	1.4.17-18 purport,
1.6.9.,	1.8.22 purport,
1.10.4 & purport	1.13.42,
1.16.4 purport,	1.16.18 purport,
1.17.3 purport,	1.19.39 purport,
3.2.8. purport,	3.2.27,
3.2.29 & purport,	3.3.4,
3.15.8,	3.16.10,
4.7.14 & purport,	4.11.27,
4.17.23 & purport,	4.127.25 purport,
4.18.8 purport,	4.18.10 & purport,

5.1 intro,	5.1.14,
5.3.33 purport,	5.15.10 & purport
5.23.3,	6.3.12,
6.3.13,	8.6.12 purport,
6.11.26 & purport,	8.8.11 & purport,
9.9.30 purport,	10.1.37,
10.8.28,	10.12.12.,
10.13.11.,	10.35.19 purport,

SB. **Srimad Bhagavatam***

10.64.13.,	10.70.10.,
11.11.18.,	11.11.43.

CS. **Shree Caitanya Shikshamrtam**

Chap. 2 sect 2   virtuous deeds.
BT (Bhaktivinoda Thakura)

SI. **Sri Isopanisad*** Intro, verse 1.

SP **Siva Purana**
- **Vidyesvara Samhita**
    13.65, 16.46-48, 20.35.
- **Rudra Samhita**
    3.47.28, 3.53.27, 5.39.51, 5.39.52,
    5.44.53
- **Kotirudra Samhita**
    6.1-4, 25.38
- **Uma Samhita**
    6.9, 6.31-34, 14.3, 14.5, 14.21-23
- **Vayaviya Samhita**
    25.23-24,25.54-55, 31.143-144, 41.14

SP RM CONV.* Room Conversation Paris. June 11 1974
Room Conversation New Orleans.
1 August 1975; by Srila Prabhupada

UN   Ujjvala Nilamani

VRC   Vraja Rata Cintamini

VVS   Vraja Vilasa Stava

* These titles are available from The Bhaktivedanta Book Trust

BIBLIOGRAPHY

Animal Traction.
Written & Edited By Peter Watson 1983   Artisan Edition
The Employment of Draught Animals in Agriculture
The Food and Agriculture Org. of the United Nations - Rome 1972
Nutrition & Working Efficiency of Draught Bovines on a Norfolk Small Holding.
Jane Bartlett, Elizabeth Barrett & David Gibbon. Discussion Paper No: 127.December 1982. School of Development Studies. Unversity of East Anglia.
The Training & Management of Draught Oxen.
Jean Paul Jeanrenaud & David Gibbon. Discussion Paper No: 126.October 1984. School of Development Studies, University of East Anglia.
An Animal Drawn Tool Carrier for Small Farm Systems.
Jean Paul Jeanrenaud David Barton & David Gibbon. Discussion Paper No. 110. October 1982. School of Development Studies, University of East Anglia.
Breeding Dairy Cattle Dr John Hinks. Farming Press Limited.
Calf Rearing.
Bill Thickett, Dan Mitchell & Bryan Hallows. Farming Press Limited.
Farm Livestock. Graham Boatfield. Farming Press Limited.
Farm Crops. Graham Boatfield. Farming Press Limited.
Calculations for Agriculture & Horticulture.
Graham Boatfield, Ian Hamilton. Farming Press Limited.
Caring for Cows.
Valerie Porter. Whittet Books.
Organic Farming.
Nicholas Lampkin. Farming Press Limited.
The Complete Herbal Handbook for Farm & Stable.
Juliette de bairacli Levy. Faber & Faber Ltd
A Review of Beef in Ancient India.
Gita Press. Gorakhpur, India
Concept of Cow in the Rgveda.
Doris Srinivasan. Motital Banarsidas, India.
Cattle Ailments - Recognition & Treatment
Eddie Straiton. Farming Press Limited.
The Complete Book of Self-Sufficiency
John Seymour. Corgi Books.

INDEX

Affection: 49
Attitude:
- of herdsman: 28,52,77

Bottle feeding: 44
Breeding : 9,25
- controlled: 28, 31, 72
Breeds of cattle: 9,10
Brushing: 49
BSE: 18
Bucket Feeding: 44
Bulls:71
- potent, wandering: 4,25,27
- young: 3

Calf -housing: 12
Calves:
- young: 1
- older: 3
Care of Cows: 95, 99
- whilst being milked: 48,49
- in extended lactation: 32
Castration: 72,106
Charitable support: 35
Commercial Breeding: 31
Concentrates : 17
Cow Dung: 106
- fuel: 34
- gas: 63
- other uses for: 63-64
Cow Protection: 9,30,35,70
- importance of: 9,28,69
Cows:
- choosing the right: 7,8
- older: 3
Cow shed: 11-13
Death:
-of a cow: 24
- and burial: 24

Draught work :81
- and cows: 83
- oxen: 28, 30, 84
- training schedule: 80
Driving
- commands for: 77-78
- oxen: 84
- safety whilst: 78

Feeding: 14-21
- cows: 20
-milking time: 48
-oxen: 20
- supplementary: 20
- without grazing: 20
- working oxen: 20
Fertiliser: 34
Food:
- equivalents table: 21
Friesian: 9

Grains: 17,20
- supplementary: 20
Grass: 16
Grazing: 50

Handling: 52-54
Harnessing: 74-76, 83
Hay: 20,21
Health: 32
Herbs: 18
Herd Composition: 28, 30-33
Herding - in woods: 4,17,55
Hereditary markings: 89

Hitch cart: 81
Housing: 5,11-13,44
Holstein: 9

HOW YOU CAN HELP

Not everyone is able to find land and care for their own cows and oxen, but there are other ways in which to show you care and help towards creating a society in which Cow Protection becomes one of the fundamental pillars of our society.

£31   **Supports a Cow for one month.**
Each Donor will receive a Certificate of Support, a photograph of a Protected Cow and a newsletter.

£351   **Supports a Cow for one year.**
Each Donor will receive a Certificate of Support, a photograph of a Protected Cow and a newsletter.

£6000   **(or a Covenant of £22.50 a month)**
Supports a Cow for life.
Each Donor will receive a Certificate of Support, a regular supply of photographs, newsletters and other gifts.
A plaque will be placed on the wall of the Bhaktivedanta Manor Cow Protection Project in recognition of your support.

I would like to support a Cow for:

☐   One month   £31

☐   One year   £351

☐   Life   £6000/Covenant (£22.50)
                    (Please send Covenant Form)

Name _____

Address _____

_____

_____

_____

Cheques should be made payable to: Bhaktivedanta Manor Cow Protection Project.

Please send the completed form to:
Bhaktivedanta Manor Cow Protection Project
Hilfield Lane, Aldenham. Herts. WD2 8EZ

COW PROTECTION CENTRES BASED IN THE UK

The following farms are all known to me personally for operating Cow Protection Programmes and upholding the Vedic principles of Vegetarian Cow Husbandry.

Further information on their individual Cow Protection Programmes may be obtained direct by writing to the addresses shown below.

ISKCON
Inish Rath Island
Lisnaskea
N. Ireland
BT92 9GN

Madana Gopal
Gillo Farm
Cenarth
Newcastle Emlyn
Dyfed
SA 38 9RB

Sharitvana Dhama
Rathgorragh
Kiltegan
Co. Wicklow
Ireland.

Grove Hill Farm
Grove Hill
Hellingly
East Sussex
BN27 4HG